WIRED
FOR
RACISM?

WIRED FOR RACISM?

How Evolution and Faith
Challenge Race-Based Thinking

JAMES WOODALL
MARK ELLINGSEN

New City Press
Hyde Park, New York

In memory of the grandmothers who lived with us in childhood and helped raise us, still very much with us as they continue to shape our values to this very day.

Charlotte McKenzie

Anna Nilssen

Published by New City Press
202 Comforter Blvd.,
Hyde Park, NY 12538
www.newcitypress.com

Wired for Racism?
How Evolution and Faith Challenge Race-Based Thinking

Cover design and layout by Miguel Tejerina

Library of Congress Control Number: 2022936813

ISBN: 978-1-56548-490-0 (paper)
ISBN: 978-1-56548-492-4 (e-book)

Printed in the United States of America

Contents

Acknowledgements

We wanted to personalize what each of us has to say about the grand ladies to whom this book is dedicated.

James:

My grandmother, Rev. Dr. Charlotte McKenzie, in many ways inspired me to imagine and work to build a world where all of God's children can experience the fullness of life here on earth. From her dragging me and my siblings to church practically every day of the week and encouraging me to put actual meaning to the faith that we so often talked about on random occasions, to being intentional about the ways I engage in the work of liberation and public policy, she is the very inspiration that pushed me toward this endeavor of writing a book. She was a mental health professional, scholar, preacher, teacher, and most importantly a woman of God. Her ministry was less about the racial distinctions between people than it was about human dignity and worth. It is in that spirit that I offer my contribution to this important work.

Mark:

My grandmother, Anna Nilssen, first inspired me through love: her love for God and for me (and I also got a lot of affection from my other beloved grandmother, Sigrid). In the case of Anna, her daily Bible reading, which she continued almost to the day of her death at 102, became ever more inspirational to me over the years. She combined this love of the Word of God with her sense of God's presence in the beauty of mountains and the seashore along with her quiet but always fierce Norwegian sense of the equality of all. These influences manifested themselves in the frequent discussions of the injustice of racism in extended family gatherings of our immigrant clan. Her Norwegian- and American-born offspring frequently lamented the injustice or the craziness of how a nation that had been so good to us could treat the sons and daughters of Africa (whom the family perceived as more "American" than we were) so much worse than recent immigrants like the Nilssen clan. Overhearing and even chiming into these discussions as a child, along with Anna's spiritual heritage, certainly have shaped my life and career.

"A mind is a terrible thing to waste."
- Arthur Fletcher, United Negro College Fund

Introduction

One afternoon in the Satilla Shores neighborhood of Brunswick, Georgia, three White men—Travis McMichael, his father Gregory McMichael, and William Bryan—used their vehicles to corner Ahmaud Arbery, a twenty-five-year-old Black man, as he ran through the area on foot. The White men killed Arbery and justified what they did by claiming that they were protecting the community from a criminal. Their "savior mentality" led them to claim that they were attempting to conduct a citizen's arrest to "stop" Arbery, but the McMichaels' "White innocence" turned almost immediately to armed hatred.

This tragic event, along with the deranged commitment to kill Black people—articulated in writing by the murderer of ten African Americans in a grocery store in a Black neighborhood in Buffalo, NY, in May 2022—illustrate what we mean by "racism in the mind." Social critique often begins from an assumption that everyone understands what "racism" and "White supremacy" mean. We choose not to make that assumption, as racism takes on many different forms. Racism includes, for so many, the hypocrisy of a criminal legal system, or a public education system that deprives generations of families and communities of access to the truth of human history. It often reduces people to being both distant from what God wills for his children and from a fulfilled version of themselves, living in a society of collective cooperation.

Woodall in particular, because he is Black, recognizes all too well, the experience of grief and darkness associated with being the target of racism, the experience of the criminal hypocrisy of a public education that deprives one of access to the truth. This is the foundation for what we consider to be ontological terror, which we define as an experience in which people, particularly Black people, are expected to exist without being fully human, and which manifests in their experience of terror over police brutality and systemic inequity, just because society says that's who they are. Seeing more and more hashtags that name someone killed at the hands of state actors—the many Black men and women killed by cops, for example—only increases American society's tolerance for it. These experiences extend beyond headline cases of police brutality. They also include experiences where everyday people or their loved ones are forced to reckon with racialized violence. Living that way leaves you discouraged, disoriented, depressed, or worse—dead. Little wonder, then, that in a poll conducted by the *Washington Post* after the 2022 Buffalo murders, 75% of Black Americans said they are worried that they or someone they care about will be physically harmed because they are Black.

Imagine growing up with a single mother who must work nonstop to provide for four children and herself while your father is in prison for the rest of his life. That's Woodall's background, and he is not unique. Many Black children live this way. These children become a social project for communities that cannot offer harm-mitigating resources because they themselves are dysfunctional. Overcoming such deficits seems to depend upon becoming someone's charity case or being seen as a "miracle." In families like Woodall's, a "normal" life for young people includes poverty, pregnancy, and even prison.

As generation after generation continues to endure racism, it becomes more and more urgent to understand how we arrived at such circumstances and recognize the kinds of responses that contribute to what happens in our minds. This book will help you understand how racism appears in America today, why it keeps appearing. But it also goes beyond that. We want to tackle racism in a couple of fresh ways.

For example, have you ever thought that you might be programmed to racism by your own brain, not just by society? Racial bias is a product of social conditioning, but it also arises from the way the human brain, especially the amygdala, works. How do we address something so deeply seated in our social and biological make-up? Science does offer a way for us to understand and address our racial biases. And if the problem has both biological and social components, then biology as well as social science can offer solutions to racial bias. Both teach us that we are most human when we are cooperating across genetic and social lines. Oh, but we're not so naïve to presume that just having these fresh insights is enough to overcome racism and the *idolatry* it creates. We purposefully call racism "idolatry"—that is, devotion to a false and ultimately dehumanizing reality. And therefore countering the idol of racism requires faith.

We will lay out the many best practices for overcoming racism, as advocated by contemporary civil rights and faith leaders. In short, this book will not only offer fresh ways to understand why racism haunts us as individuals and as a society; it will also present strategies for tackling racism, including a summary of what today's Black leaders believe would help the cause. You'll find new insights as well as down-to-earth practical ideas.

One of us (James Woodall) is a millennial Black Baptist preacher, a civil rights leader in the south, a public policy associate of the Southern Center for Human Rights, and the former president of the Georgia NAACP. The other (Mark Ellingsen) is a baby boomer, a White minister (Norwegian-American Lutheran), and a professor of Church history at the largest historic Black seminary in the nation. Both of us are deeply invested in going beyond simply naming and analyzing the obvious (or even the not-so-obvious) about racism. We are equally committed to drawing on the solution-based strategies we can employ within our respective communities and spheres of influence. Our goal is to deconstruct the mind's biases, rebuild our human consciousness, destroy the idolatry, and ultimately suggest ways to free the land so all of God's creatures can embrace their full selves.

We began working together at the Interdenominational Theological Center in Atlanta, when Ellingsen was teaching a course on the history of Christian thought and Woodall was a graduate student. As Ellingsen learned of Woodall's role in the NAACP and his knowledge of the various civil rights organizations' programs, these roles began to reverse. Then began a dialogue on how history and theology might address the pressing issues of racism and freedom today. That dialogue has led us to write this book. The more we exchange experiences, ideas, and solutions, the more we realize that, despite our obvious differences in age, ethnicity, and experience, our conversation and our collaboration can enrich the world around us.

In the classroom we have both labored intensely to learn more about the nature of faith and how to use our agency as faith leaders to engage with and organize our brothers and sisters to build a more just world. Through innumerable hours of debate and dialogue, we have come to better understand each other. As members of distinct ethnic communities, we come to the table with cultural understandings that contribute to the broader story of resistance which, when we share it, gets us closer to us challenging the foundation of racism.

Our shared experience is a vibrant illustration of the "how" by which we embrace the power of cooperation that is embedded in our genes. *Wired for Racism?* demonstrates how both evolution and faith teach that we have this power. Human beings thrive when we collaborate and co-create. It's the very nature of the way *Homo sapiens* evolved as a species, how the human mind works, and how Christians believe God created us. When you play and work together, when you start collaborating in ways where there's a balance of power, you deconstruct the deficiencies that prevent the full affirmation of humanity.

Our relationship illustrates another of our findings. Our budding friendship has by no means ended racism in America (or anywhere else). Our experience, as powerful as it is, shows that racism will not be ended merely by cooperating with friends of another race, understanding the evolutionary dynamics of race, or sharing a common faith. That's why this book will not just stop at struggling to grasp what "racism in the mind" means. To bring about social, political, and economic justice, readers like you need to join us in the trenches. This book will give you some suggestions. But before getting to what to do *about* racism, you need to get a handle on what it *is*.

The Nature of Racism

A deficiency in the sort of cooperation we are trying to promote leads to a religious idolatry in which people begin to act as if they themselves are ultimate beings, which then leads to a categorical denial of the divinity of God. This idolatry and denial come about when one human being denies another human being the divinely-bestowed right to power, love, and a sound mind because such freedom is perceived as an impediment to

13

the oppressor's wellbeing. In America, this is the essence of White supremacy. And when such a denial is based primarily on the false conditions of racial categories—especially using the White/Black distinction—it is called racism.

We also must address this problem: Many people do not recognize their own idolatry because of their own self-perception of unarmed innocence. They convince themselves, for example, that charity and mission trips to third-world countries, often accompanied by a virtue-signaling acknowledgement of their White privilege, are all they need to prove that they are not racist. After all, they have Black friends.

We agree with Ibram X. Kendi and the tenets of Critical Race Theory at least on this point: The very fact that racial categories exist sustains racial idolatry.[1] Racial categories, which are primarily Black and White, have no biological basis. Rather, they were fabricated to isolate sociopolitical groups and render them as "other." In *Beyond Ontological Blackness*, Victor Anderson describes Black existence as a reaction to the racist standard of whiteness. If Anderson is correct, and we believe he is, seeking to dismantle racism and its essential component, White supremacy, is a truly revolutionary—and perhaps suicidal—undertaking. Destroying racism and White supremacy are acts of revolutionary suicide insofar as those who seek to do so often face threats of either violence or ostracism. When you confront oppressive structures you can expect this sort of backlash. "Revolutionary suicide," a term first described by Huey P. Newton (co-founder of the Black Panther Party) in his

1.   Ibram X. Kendi, *How to Be an Antiracist* (New York: One World, 2019); Richard Delgado and Jean Stefancic, *Critical Race Theory: An Introduction* (New York: New York University Press, 2017), pp. 9–10, 21.

book of the same name, doesn't mean that individuals literally kill themselves; rather they intentionally risk both life and livelihood for the sake of freedom and justice for all.

What then do we intend to accomplish by calling for eliminating racial categories? We want to end the use of these categories as justification for White supremacy. We have no intention of diminishing African American culture, which has preserved and adapted the cultural riches that people brought with them from Africa—such as its music, spirituality, sense of mystery, politeness, and veneration of elders. We don't want to see these cultural goods and heritage of Woodall's brothers and sisters explained away or reduced to mere reactions to White racism, nor do we propose that Ellingsen and his fellow Norwegians here in America give up their characteristic humility, love of nature, sense of adventure, and fierce sense of the equality of all. Indeed, we don't want Americans of any background—Italian, Hispanic, Irish, Jewish, Asian, Arab or any other culture—to feel that to overcome racism they must compromise the values of their country of origin. We acknowledge that the process of Americanization (and its "whitening") has allowed only a few to retain their cultural gifts beyond a couple of generations after the family has immigrated. But diversity is a good thing; diversity itself does not cause division or place obstacles to cooperation. We want to affirm the Norwegians' perspective: "Our culture and land is so small. We need others to make our world bigger."

While we want to celebrate diversity, we also want to contend with those themes of Critical Race Theory that might be construed as entailing a separation of people based on racial lines. Our own collaboration on this book is a witness to our saying "no" to consideration of racial categories as having ultimate importance. Critical Race Theory, however, rightly warns that White people who identify with the cause of Black equality often do so only when their interests converge with those of Black people.[2] That insight is also reflected in the United States Constitution and in James Madison's *The Federalist Papers*.[3] We'll also show that in the big picture the self-interests of people typically converge in the broader best interest of all people; the full power of humanity is revealed when we cooperate with each other, when we find ways to enhance the convergence of our self-interests.

We point out other noticeable components of racism. We recognize that the affected parties are often silenced not only through the dehumanizing violence of racism and White supremacy; they are also silenced when White men and women deny that they could be oppressors because they cannot comprehend how or why they may be involved in a wickedness so foul that it leads to denying the very existence of the non-White "other." It would be foolish not to acknowledge the real-world impact such denials can have. Numerous examples throughout human history tell the story of sociopaths who either refused to acknowledge the failures of a once-sound mind or openly embraced their sinful ways and so cost others their lives.

Our book draws on resources of Christian faith and of science—particularly evolutionary biology—in ways that neither authors like Ibram X. Kendi and Victor Anderson nor Critical Race Theory consider. We will explore how brain

---

2.   This idea is elaborated by Derrick Bell in "Who's Afraid of Critical Race Theory," *University of Illinois Law Review* 4 (1995): pp. 893–910.

3.   James Madison, "No. 51," in *The Federalist Papers* (New York: Penguin, 1961), pp. 323–324.

functions and racism are linked, and how racism is embedded (at least in the "animal parts") in our minds. What's also fresh in this book is how we demonstrate that the agendas of leading human rights movements, such as Black Lives Matter and Movement for Black Lives, are not radical at all, but rather are logical extensions of evolutionary biology and of Christian faith understood in terms of God's love for all human beings.

Where We Are Headed

As we identify the dynamics of racism in the mind, it is necessary to explore the dynamics of racism in society as well. Other authors have touched on the connection between neurobiology and racism. For example, *Bias, Racism and the Brain: How We Got Where We Are and What Needs to Happen Next* (Oxford Brain Institute, 2020) by Jason Greer and Phil Dixon explains how our brains are telling us stories about the outside world that may not be true. Jonathan Kahn's recently published *Race on the Brain: What Implicit Bias Gets Wrong about the Struggle for Racial Justice* (Columbia University Press, 2017) makes the case that reducing racism to just brain dynamics dodges the actual problems and makes things too easy for those who would dismiss racism lightly. So while we will address the neurobiological components of racism and racial bias, we acknowledge that challenging our natural biases on an individual level will not overcome racism—that effort requires societal change, including dismantling systems that prop up racism.

Our closing chapters consider the implications of these scientific findings and how they can interact with the role reason, politics, and faith can play in fighting racism. But we also make clear that the institutional structures which benefit from the forces of racial idolatry would continue to operate even if the mind were not susceptible to racism.

From politics and poverty to economics and education, sinful social structures reinforce our mental tendencies, thus creating schisms of mental instability and spiritual degradation that keep us further away from the divine nature of soundness, love, and power. That's why our first chapter addresses racism in criminal justice, housing, business, the natural environment, education, voting, and the culture. We want to place front and center the realities of racism and their impact on people's daily lives. We intend for readers to come to understand and embrace Black people as human beings, while also understanding why White people are uncomfortable when they are labeled as racist. The chapter offers this analysis as an introduction to how racism functions. Protestations of innocence by White people keep racist systems in place. We need to challenge this, to make clear that racism is not just a practice of prejudice by individual White people but is also a system in which all people participate, whether they know it or not. White people can offer many ultimately unsupportable reasons for denying their complicity in our present racist system.

Our second chapter explains the complexity of how racism functions and the kind of idolatry it promotes. We'll discuss how some African Americans who have "made it" in the present system continue naively to support it because rejecting it would mean abandoning their comfortable position. We also consider the ontology of race; that is, the philosophical dynamics of racial oppression that use racial stereotypes to render minorities as "other," separating them from the rest of humanity.

The third chapter presents lessons regarding the connection between racism and the human brain. Neurobiology confirms that we're all racists, that we all get uptight with people who don't share our gene pool or at least are unfamiliar to us. When you feel threatened, whether you are White or Black, certain parts of the brain make you inclined to fight-or-flight behavior. White fear of Blacks and Black fear of whites underlie the violent tendencies on both sides. Since we are more comfortable with our own, in a society with most of the advantages given to White citizens it is more likely whites will tend to open doors for and collaborate with others who are not perceived as terrorizing. The chapter explores the deep reasons for the depths of racism. Racial discrimination is linked to brain dynamics. But as we show, merely overcoming our innate biases with better brain control of our emotions will not help us defeat racism. Overcoming racism also requires challenging power dynamics, racial stereotypes, and structural racism.

This background illuminates a way out of the mess we're in. The fourth chapter draws on lessons taught by evolution and the contribution religion might make to overcoming racism. Both evolutionary studies and research on the role of religion offer some useful approaches to the issues of racism. The unique development of the human brain is the development of a large frontal lobe that allows *Homo sapiens* to control functions that animals cannot. Human beings are gifted with remarkable abilities to suppress anxiety about strangers and instead to cooperate with other creatures different from ourselves. These cooperative abilities are explained by the economist Heather McGhee, whose book *The Sum of Us: What Racism Costs Everyone and How We Can Prosper Together* (One World, 2021) explains the benefits for everyone of overcoming racism. Religion also contributes to brain development and so contributes to our superior abilities to cooperate. Practicing religion, walking in faith, can enhance our cooperative efforts in fighting racism. On the other hand, when we close the doors to cooperation, we make ourselves less than human. Our chapter closes by drawing out the implications of these insights for formulating anti-racist strategies.

We also offer sobering thoughts about the difficulties that this work entails. However, through the experience of God's grace, which the latest findings of evolutionary biologists suggest is manifested to all people of faith, we can reach a true resolution of racism. These truths—that *all* men and women are created both equal *and* in God's image—are made evident. All members of *Homo sapiens* have an innate propensity to cooperate with their fellow human beings. Blocking such cooperation with racial barriers diminishes our humanity.

The last chapter offers reflections on short-term and long-term strategies for beating racism. Our reflections on faith provide a strong framework for understanding and great motivation for making happen what we propose. Believers and non-believers alike can cooperate in destroying racism. We will draw upon the practical wisdom of venerable civil rights organizations and Black leaders, as well principles from the American constitutional system as described in *The Federalist Papers*. As do proponents of Critical Race Theory, James Madison and Alexander Hamilton expect that some will attempt to appropriate power, caution us that we cannot succeed by individual action alone, and remind us that mutual self-interest is the basis of all coalitions. Their political principles, like Christian religious principles, provide a system and a perspective for keeping ourselves in check while striving for justice through compromise.

Not everyone, even among Black intellectuals, agrees with what we propose. Some, like Robert L. Woodson and his 1776 Unites project and their book *Red, White, and Black:*

Rescuing American History from Revisionists and Race Hustlers (Emancipation Books, 2021) challenge the idea of systemic racism. Though we do agree with them that our constitutional system can serve in the struggle against racism, we maintain that the system in its present form is racist.

We've explained where we are headed and why we wish to go there. Our first challenge, then, is to convince you about the realities of racism and help you acknowledge it and empathize with its victims in new ways. Chapter one seeks to help you empathize with the pain, anxiety, and anger of Black people in America, and help you understand why it's justified. It is the longest chapter in the book because we recognize that systemic racism is both complex and saturates every day of our lives. We explore White guilt and those who protest their innocence, and how even though their claim of innocence cannot be justified, it does satisfy certain psychological and political needs. Against a backdrop of mutual understanding, readers—Black, white, and every other category presented—should be prepared to do what our Creator and evolution have designed us to do. Hopefully, someday we can write a revision or sequel celebrating how this book's insights on faith, evolution, and politics have been integrated into American society, and this first chapter on racial idolatry can be a whole lot shorter.

Chapter 1

The Facts about Racism and
Why We Still Bow before the Throne of Race

To grapple with racism, we must contend with many factors, including social matters, and not just neurobiology. The human brain does spark anxiety-producing reactions to people of a different ethnicity, but that alone does not explain racism. Jonathan Kahn, who has studied the phenomenon of racism, notes that analyzing racism in terms of brain dynamics "give[s] us too easy an out for feeling good about our stand on racism. Everybody has implicit biases, and since we can't consciously control these biases, it feels like they are not our fault." Kahn also worries that when racism is reduced to a "material thing" that can be observed, we are likely to think it can be measured and addressed with cultural competence training, that all we need to do is "work on ourselves."[1]

Dismantling racism is not just about changing individual attitudes. There are larger structural and institutional forces that shape inequality. That's why it's important to examine some hard facts about racism to supplement what we learn from faith, neurobiology, sociology, politics, and economics.

Where to begin? In the introduction we alluded to the way racism is experienced in the Black community—living

---

1. Jonathan Kahn, "Viewing racism as a biology problem totally ignores the real forces driving it," Center for Health Journalism, April 17, 2018.

with the threat of violence from police, the long-term effects of incarceration on families, the very fact of racial categories and their effect on those who are considered minorities, diminishing the impact of racism on the Black community by claiming "White innocence." We need to address in a particular way two problems of White innocence: the feeling that since I am not a racist, a lot of what is happening isn't my fault; and the belief that success by some Black Americans is proof that the system works and is not racist.

Those who press for a focus on less controversial topics keep chanting, "Why does everything have to be about race?" They maintain that racism is a thing of the past, that the world has moved beyond it. After all, slavery was abolished through the Emancipation Proclamation of 1863. Jim Crow ended with the passage of the Civil Rights Act of 1964 and the Voting Rights Act of 1965. Even the election of former US President Barack H. Obama is said to be evidence of our having entered a post-racial society. These people agree that race had been used to exclude and dehumanize *back then*, but now we are beyond that barbarism.

The tension is obvious, as the very premise of this book rejects the idea that we have moved beyond racism at all. People seeing each other as human beings is a start at getting to that post-racist society. The challenge, though, is that the individual daily experience of Black people is filled with discriminatory mistreatment, economic exploitation, and even sociopolitical neglect. From being pulled over because you "look suspicious" if you're driving a nice car to not having access to healthcare, quality education, or even healthy food, the exclusion of those considered "other" have far-reaching implications which we explore in this chapter. The inequities that Black individuals and communities face are not just statistics; these are the experiences and lives of real human beings.

We can start with what Americans themselves have said recently. In June 2020, at the height of the protests over the police killings of Black men, a Monmouth University poll reported that 76% of Americans (including 71% of whites) identified racial discrimination as a "big problem." Although most Black Americans have known that all along, that's news for many White Americans. Readers also probably knew that racism hadn't gone away long before they chose to read this book. But many White people consider the problem of racism to be somebody else's problem, because they do not think they are racist.

Even whites who were enraged early in the summer of 2020 got over their anger quickly (as is so common with the American public). A Democracy Fund + UCLA Nationscape poll revealed that while 43% of White Americans had deemed race a big problem during the height of the George Floyd protests, this number had fallen to 23% by August 2020, a rate that has continued to decline.[2] Likewise, on May 22, 2021, *The New York Times* reported that the percentage of the White population who supported the Black Lives Matter movement had declined by 8% (from 60% to 52%) since early in 2020, and by 20% since its height in the summer of 2020, which is why we consider it necessary to provide readers with evidence of America's racism.[3]

---

2. Reported in Heather McGhee, *The Sum of Us* (New York: One World, 2021), p. 238.

3. Jennifer Churdy and Hakeen Jefferson, "Support for Black Lives Matter Movement Surged Last Year. Did It Last?," *The New York Times*, May 22, 2021.

The coronavirus pandemic exacerbated this tension. As the world was forced to suspend its normal way of life, Black people in the United States had less access to testing, treatment, and vaccinations than other populations—something that the media and public health experts pointed out continuously throughout the pandemic. The pandemic also had a disproportionate economic impact on Black communities, primarily because the existing disparities in wealth only grew greater.

For example, in the second quarter of 2021, the US Bureau of Labor Statistics reported that White full-time workers earned $1,012 per week and Black workers $799, a difference of over $10,000 per year. And though it was an economic period of difficulty for every demographic, this type of disparity isn't unusual: the bureau reported that "between January 1972 and December 2019, other than during the aftermaths of recessions the [Black] unemployment rate stayed at or above twice the White rate."[4] A 2020 study reported by Statista even says that Black college-educated workers, on average, make 89% of what their White college-educated peers make.

To add insult to injury, some states opted out of the federal pandemic unemployment benefits program, again with a disproportionate impact on African Americans. The State of Georgia, for example, saw as much as 60% of the pre-pandemic labor force turn to unemployment programs, including a disproportionate number of Black workers.[5] Ending this relief forced millions of Black and White workers to return to

---

4. Prior to January 1972, the U.S. Bureau of Labor Statistics did not collect data on Black and other non White populations.
5. Ray Khalfani, "State of Working Georgia: Pandemic Job Numbers Are Improving, but Inequitably," Georgia Budget and Policy Institute, April 20, 2021.

their jobs, of which many pay less than a living wage and have maintained pre-pandemic wage levels without cost-of-living adjustments. The Congressional Budget Office calculates that even by 2025, seventeen million workers will still be paid less than $15 an hour. These numbers represent human lives, and for many of these families, the failure to acknowledge the harm in the disparity of wages and unemployment benefits further demonstrates why racism is still alive and well.

Racism in the Criminal Justice System

The American criminal legal system has become more responsible for promoting and sustaining racism in contemporary society than any other state institution. From the Black Codes of the Post-Reconstruction South and Jim Crow to the school-to-prison pipeline and mass incarceration, this complex system of legal and correctional control continues to impact both Black men and women, and poor people of every race. Consider the simple fact that, as of 2017, Black people made up a third of the US prison population while only comprising about 12% of the entire population.[6]

The role that racism plays in the criminal legal process begins with the dangers that often surface during encounters between law enforcement and individual citizens. In many communities, the effectiveness of policing is measured by the number of traffic tickets written and of people arrested. According to the ACLU of Georgia, in 2017, Black people made up 51% of the population in Atlanta, yet made up 87% of all arrests. Police practices such as these amplify the racist hypocrisy

---

6. John Gramlich, "The gap between the number of blacks and whites in prison is shrinking," Pew Research Center, April 30, 2019.

because it becomes less about maintaining public safety and more about maintaining control over human bodies, especially Black bodies.

Some may dismiss concern over punishment for people who are convicted of crimes because they are "getting what they deserve." But when you consider wealth-based disparity in terms of legal representation and access to resources that aid in defending oneself against criminal charges, racism is evident and is partly the reason the criminal legal system disparately impacts Black people. "Innocent people are choosing to plead guilty, rather than 'gamble' with their chances of getting justice through trial," according to the National Registry of Exonerations.[7]

Often the supposition that crime is more likely to occur in Black communities is used to justify considering Black people as suspects because they are allegedly more inclined to exhibit criminal behavior—a narrative that is rooted in a sociopolitical ideology that Black people are inherently sinful, violent, and criminal. The official justification for this approach to law enforcement can be found in a model developed in the 1990s by the NYPD called "CompStat," based on the concept that police should use statistics to predict where and how crime is most likely to happen in order to stop crimes before they occur. Proponents of this approach argue that there are desirable implications resulting from this policy in terms of efficient allocation of police resources and crime prevention. But problems arise when this method is applied to policing neighborhoods of mostly Black residents. Everyone within that community then becomes a suspect because of physical appearance, not because of their own actions. When crime

---

7.   "The Disappearing Trial," Summary Document, Fair Trials, p. 14.

occurs in predominantly White neighborhoods, Black people are often accused, even if they live in that community. This is how racial profiling emerges from the prevailing paradigm of police work.

At least three other dynamics can be added to explain the racism inherent in modern police work. According to Louis Dekmar, former president of the International Association of Chiefs of Police, if a higher number of police officers are deployed in Black neighborhoods that have more crime, then people in those neighborhoods are more likely to be accused of committing crimes than those who live in less-policed neighborhoods.[8]

Psychologist Jennifer Eberhardt, a leading consultant for police who seek to avoid prejudice, refers to a second harmful dynamic in this system: the unconscious prejudice of law enforcement officers, which leads to the expectation that people will give them unconditional deference for simply being officers, despite people sometimes refusing to do just that.[9] In addition, White officers (and even some Black officers influenced by negative images of Black people) are more likely to have their amygdala (the part of the brain which, as we'll note later, is the seat of emotion) in overdrive when they encounter Black people, and so are more likely to make an arrest or pull the trigger.

Finally, the excessive number of police shootings of Black people is evidenced by data provided by Statista, which reported in May 2022 that from 2015–2022 there were more than two times as many Black people as whites in

---

8. Louis Dekmar, private interview, April 2, 2021.
9. Jennifer Eberhardt, *Biased: Uncovering the Hidden Prejudice That Shapes What We See, Think, and Do* (New York: Viking), 2019.

law-enforcement-involved shootings. The preceding statistics and our analysis of the CompStat model of policing make it obvious that racial profiling is embedded.

Disparate Prosecution and Sentencing

Legal practices such as mandatory minimum sentencing have had a severe negative impact on criminal justice in this country. Dating back as far as Reconstruction and earlier, the US legal system has been weaponized to institute racism. Slave patrols in the antebellum South led to black codes after the Emancipation Proclamation, as White Southerners sought new methods to detain and dehumanize those who were newly freed from state-sponsored slavery. These methods often included prohibitions of acts of "moral turpitude," which allowed states to criminalize behaviors in a way that targeted Negroes. Legal scholar Michelle Alexander noted in her recent book *The New Jim Crow: Mass Incarceration in the Age of Colorblindness* that "the nature of the criminal justice system has changed. It is no longer primarily concerned with the prevention and punishment of crime, but rather with the management and control of the dispossessed."[10]

In comparison to White Americans, Black individuals are prosecuted more frequently and sentenced with violent precision, such as when a prosecutor stacks indictments to coerce plea deals and advocates for longer sentences. A person who is accused of a criminal offense is less likely to be acquitted of any or all charges due to the common prosecutorial practice of stacking indictments. In order to get more

---

10.   Michelle Alexander, *The New Jim Crow: Mass Incarceration in the Age of Colorblindness* (New York: The New Press, 2010), p. 111.

convictions, prosecutors sometimes charge a defendant with multiple offenses in order to increase the probability of a conviction of any sort. This practice has no concern for whether or not the accused is in fact guilty of all the charges. A plea deal is then offered and is more likely to be accepted by the accused in hopes that he or she won't spend a long time in prison. The differences in determining sentences do not reflect differences in criminal activity, but rather differences in race. According to the NAACP, "Blacks and whites use drugs at similar rates, but the imprisonment rate of Blacks for drug charges is almost six times that of whites."[11] The Death Penalty Information Center reported in January 2022 that 41.3% of inmates on death row are Black, while only about 12% of the American population is Black.[12]

This data reflects only the surface of racial bias in this nation. Based on 2016–2018 polls by the National Longitudinal Study of Adolescent Health, between 48% and 52% of young Black men (nearly all of whom are from low-income neighborhoods) can expect to serve time in prison.[13]

This disparity is not surprising when we consider the imbalance in judicial sentences by race. In 2017, the United States Sentencing Commission reported that sentences given to Black inmates in the federal judicial system are nearly 20% longer than sentences given to whites for comparable crimes.[14]

11. "Criminal Justice Fact Sheet," NAACP, naacp.org/resources/criminal-justice-fact-sheet.

12. "Racial Demographics," Death Penalty Information Center, January 1, 2022.

13. Nathaniel Lewis, "Mass Incarceration" (People's Policy Project, n.d.).

14. German Lopez, "Report: black men get longer sentences for the same federal crime as White men," *Vox*, Nov.17, 2017.

Even the rate of fatal police shootings in the U.S. shows a large difference based on ethnicity. Among Black Americans, the rate of fatal police shootings between 2015 and June 2020 stood at thirty-one per million of the population. In comparison, White Americans were victims in about thirteen fatal police shootings per million of the population. Another way to put it: According to a study conducted by Mapping Police Violence in 2021, 28% of Americans shot by police were Black.

Political scientist Wilfred Reilly of the Black conservative group 1776 Unites seeks to downplay these figures by arguing that criminals are statistically more likely to be Black than white.[15] But in making this argument, Reilly does not take into account the racism evident in statistical policing, trials, and sentencing as noted above. Moreover, as will be presented in chapter three, the human brain has a neurobiological bent toward racism that must be countered.

The racism in our justice system surely makes its presence known in the economy. For example, the prison system has an increasing number of private, for-profit corporations running our jails. Because jail populations are heavily skewed Black, for-profit prisons are another example of a white-controlled system making money from Black unpaid labor.

None of this is surprising, given the way the media portrays Black people and social as well as criminal indictments of Black men for being in the "wrong place at the wrong time." In chapter three, we'll look at how our brains can hype up anxieties about those who appear different. When White society gives those anxieties free rein and fosters them through the

---

15. Wilfred Reilly, "A Positive Vision: The Agenda of 1776," in *Red, White, and Black*, ed. Robert L. Woodson (New York: Post Hill Press, 2021), pp. 5–6.

media, it's little wonder the American system and public operate under the belief that "those people" should be put away.

Racism in the Market

Even when Black Americans are employed, they do not earn as much as whites. It is true that the Black worker saw significant increases in wage earnings from 1940 to 1960, but as factory jobs began to disappear, wage growth saw minimal increases over the next sixty years.[16] This is at least related to the kinds of jobs held by Black workers, but as we have already noted, even Black workers with college degrees make considerably less than their White counterparts with similar educational backgrounds. The economic disparities between Blacks and whites in America has long been an urgent challenge. Efforts like the Moral Monday movement and the Poor People's Campaign, led by Rev. Dr. William Barber and Rev. Dr. Liz Theoharis respectively, exemplify this commitment through their urging of elected officials to increase the federal minimum wage to $15/hour, a move that is having some impact and could substantially improve the standard of living for millions of people in this country.

Due to inaction by elected officials in addressing economic failures and racial inequities, however, the American capitalistic enterprise has produced, by far, the greatest form of racist idolatry (the commitment to furthering the interests of one's own ethnic group above all else). Many of the systems within White society have developed through the transactional nature of commerce and are rooted in such idolatry. We make

---

16. Andrew Hacker, *Two Nations: Black and White, Separate, Hostile, Unequal* (New York: Scribner, 1992), pp. 107–108.

other people "things"; we make them "others" and define our-selves as superior to the "other." This is the essence of idolatry.

Government Complicity

The US government sanctioned slavery from the outset, and the federal government's abandoning Reconstruction allowed the states to pass and enforce Jim Crow laws. Woodrow Wilson segregated the federal workforce. Government complicity in racism continued with Franklin D. Roosevelt's New Deal. This policy gave certain people during that generation a leg up while others were excluded from the available economic opportunities.

When Social Security was first created, people in agricultural and housekeeping jobs—an overwhelming majority of whom were Black—were not eligible. As a result, they were excluded from Social Security benefits. It is true that changes have been implemented in the program since then to include all categories of people, but the delay in access does impact the potential for generational economic parity between racial demographics. The extra money spent by these excluded families could have instead been used to save or invest, similarly to their White counterparts. This is certainly an area for which reparation might be considered—more on that in the final chapter.

The New Deal was just the beginning of the racial disparities in the economy. We have already noted the Black-White wage disparity and higher unemployment rates for Black people. Another piece of disturbing data has been identified by Jamal Simmons.[17] He has noted that most major American

17. Jamal Simmons, "The 4 Percent Problem," *Democracy: A Journal of Ideas*, May 4, 2021.

institutions employ Black people to be at most 4% of their total staff. For example, only 2.4% of partners of Paul, Weiss, Rifkind, Wharton & Garrison, a multinational private equity law firm made up of over 1,000 attorneys, are Black. From 2005 through 2018 only 4.1% of US Supreme Court law clerks were Black. Only 3.7% of the tenured faculty at Yale, 3% of executives at Facebook, and 4% of executives at Amazon are Black. Even in the military, only 4.9% of the military's most senior leaders are Black. All of this is to say that there is not a single sector in the American economy which this disparity of representation and inclusion does not affect.

Another practice which we might consider that has been harmful for Black people in particular is state lotteries. State lotteries effectively reduce how much wealthier people must pay in taxes by producing revenue on lottery sales to poor and working-class people, who make up the lottery's primary market. Data from the US Census Bureau's population surveys for all fifty states (1976–1995) demonstrate that a significant portion of the increase in income inequality (i.e., the discrepancy in real income between the wealthiest and poorest segments of the population) over the twenty-year period was attributable to the increasing prevalence of state lotteries.

In fact, African Americans spend five times more on lottery tickets than White Americans.[18] To be clear, participation in the lottery is not mandatory. The point we raise, however, is the exploitative nature of state-sponsored campaigns that draw upon the racist dimensions of our society to produce profit margins from the backs of those most impacted by their conditions. If we keep doing business as we have, does this not

---

18.   Alvin Chang, "4 ways the lottery preys on the poor," *Vox*, January 13, 2016.

still perpetuate racism? We believe it does, and this racism even extends to people's ability to find affordable and available housing.

Housing Discrimination (Red-Lining)

The American housing crisis also highlights the impact of systemic racism. Policies such as the G.I. Bill—officially called the Servicemen's Readjustment Act of 1944—were designed to prevent Black and other non-White people from being able to take advantage of programs approved to increase home ownership and economic health of communities. From devious provisions and physical intimidation to rejections of mortgage applications and discharging Black veterans dishonorably without cause, these strategies were effective in decreasing access for some while others saw exponential benefits. These practices led to the housing boom for the White members of the so-called Greatest Generation, which still has an impact on the wealth gap today.

Of course, segregated housing in the Southern United States is a vestige of the Jim Crow era. But discrimination in the housing market can be traced specifically to the New Deal era and the creation of the Federal Housing Administration (FHA). The FHA was intended to make homeownership easier for families by guaranteeing mortgages in certain neighborhoods. Some neighborhoods, primarily those with mostly Black residents, did not qualify for these mortgages, and consequently were denied equal access under the law. Homeownership is one of the most effective methods for building generational wealth. But the disparate practice of housing discrimination led to an ever-increasing wealth gap that continues to widen even today.

These dynamics have led real estate companies and banks to appraise the property values in Black neighborhoods at lower values than comparable homes in White neighborhoods. Housing in northern urban areas has also been victimized by racism, increasingly since the 1950s.

The city of the nineteenth century and the first half of the twentieth century was a paradoxical mix of (often ethnic) neighborhoods. One never was too far away from high culture—and sometimes loose living—in which one's ethnic origin ultimately melted. Yet the whole time, the old ethnic neighborhood was just across town or over the river. In the city, it was not hard to be "ethnic" and American at the same time. Outside the neighborhood, the diverse citizens of the city shared a lot in common, and sometimes even went to school together and worked together without ceasing to be Irish, Italian, Jewish, Dutch, Norwegian, Chinese, or African back in the hood.

In this context there was significant goodwill toward race relations on all sides in the decades immediately following World War II. Even ethnic neighborhoods, for all the anxiety about losing a certain appearance when immigrants and Black people started moving in, remained committed to the principles of fair play that they believed their new country stood for. (To this day, many of these White ethnic groups know it is not Blacks and Hispanics who are causing them the problems they now face.) Jackie Robinson's legacy in Brooklyn was very much alive and contributing to these feelings of commonality and the need for justice.

Social reformers committed to the cause of integration in the 1960s may have made some mistakes by advocating for and engineering assaults on the ethnic neighborhood as somehow embodying racism. Cities began to change as businesses went elsewhere, because the mills either closed with the decline of the old ethnic character of the neighborhood or were relocated. The businesses that replaced them— in finance, communications, real estate, tourism, and entertainment—did not provide jobs for the masses. White flight, which had begun with the first wave of business relocations, continued with even more force. As communities deteriorated, even people with jobs in the city moved to the suburbs, and what remained was poverty.

Residential segregation translates into economic segregation and heightens the impact that vanishing resources had on communities that were often home to mainly Black residents. These dynamics have been well documented and discussed by Sheryll Cashin in her book *White Space, Black Hood*. Now, as those same communities begin to experience gentrification, young professionals return to metropolitan communities to invest in and "revitalize" neighborhoods. This practice has led to even more racial segregation: a University of California study reported in 2021 that 80% of the larger US metropolitan regions were more segregated in 2019 than in 1990.[19] This isolation breeds more suspicion and racism.

It is important to reiterate that Black neighborhoods were not as profitable as others. Together, all of the majority Black neighborhoods in the United States contain 3.2 million owner-occupied homes worth an estimated $609 billion. But those homes would collectively be worth $156 billion more if not for the lower value that comes with the perceptions associated with being in a majority Black neighborhood. In fact, for the last eight years, a house in a majority Black neighborhood

---

19. Stephen Menendian, Samir Gambhir, and Arthur Gailes, "The Roots of Structural Racism Project," Othering & Belonging Institute, University of California-Berkeley, June 21, 2021.

loses between 20 to 30% of its value compared to its appraisal in a majority White neighborhood.[20] Since family wealth, in most American families, is tied to the value of property owned, the racism of the American economy robs economic power from families in racially segregated communities. Further, it is much harder for Black people to access resources to become homeowners, even if they want to buy in a predominantly Black neighborhood.

The Center for Investigative Reporting found in 2018—while controlling for a variety of factors including income, loan amount, and neighborhood—that people of color were more likely than whites to be denied a conventional home loan in sixty-one metro areas, including Atlanta, Detroit, and Washington, D.C. Data from the Home Mortgage Disclosure Act in 2020 also showed that Black mortgage applicants were denied 80% more often than White applicants. In Philadelphia, Black applicants were nearly three times as likely as whites to be denied a home loan. And recent evidence shows that financiers typically charge borrowers of color eight points higher interest rates than they charge White borrowers.[21]

Readers who share our common moral human sensibilities should be getting angry, as we feel and see the pressures of generational poverty leading to negative outcomes as diverse as fear, drug use, incarceration, and even slower brain development. We have a system designed for racial inequity—it thrives on and profits from disparity—and people's lives are made worse because of it.

---

20. Dana Anderson, "The Price of Racial Bias," Redfin News, April 20, 2021.

21. Aaron Glantz and Emmanuel Martinez, "For people of color, banks are shutting the door to homeownership," Reveal News, February 15, 2018.

Racism in Business

Let's turn to Black-owned businesses, and the disparity in loans, which are given at a much larger percentage to whites seeking financing for new business start-ups, compared to their Black counterparts. The US Small Business Administration reports the most common source of start-up financing for new businesses comes from business loans made by banks, credit unions, or other financial institutions. Almost 19% of White business owners received a loan from a bank or other financial institution to start their business, compared to 15.2% of Black or African American business owners.[22] Why? Banks don't loan freely to Black entrepreneurs.

The Black farmer has been badly hurt too. The number of Black farmers in the U.S. has declined by 90% since 1920, now comprising fewer than fifty thousand American farmers out of a total of 3.4 million, a fact related to proven discrimination in US Department of Agriculture (USDA) loan policies, even by their own admission in a report on the USDA National Commission on Small Farms.[23] There have been attempts to address this discrimination extending across generations, such as the *Pigford v. Glickman* class-action suit for rampant discrimination in which Black farmers reached a $1 billion settlement with the USDA. But it will take more if the Black farmer is ever to get justice.

---

22. Alicia Robb, "Financing Patterns and Credit Market Experiences: A Comparison by Race and Ethnicity for U.S. Employer Firms," U.S. Small Business Administration Office of Advocacy, February 1, 2018.
23. Jennifer Fahy, "How Heirs' Property Fueled the 90 Percent Decline in Black-Owned Farmland," farmaid.org, February 28, 2022.

As we began to write this book, the Emergency Relief for Farmers of Color Act (sponsored by Senator Raphael Warnock of Georgia), which would help farmers of color obtain loan debt and pandemic relief, was passed by Congress and signed into law by President Joe Biden. However, few of these attempts have been successful due to White farmers challenging these actions based on equal protection claims under the Constitution, and as such this relief has been halted by legal inquiries into whether such a reparative investment is constitutional.

The state of Black farmers, who now account for only 2% of the nation's farms, displays the American system's bias against the Black working class in general. We have already noted how the job market is more challenging for Black workers, considering wages, job placement, and upward mobility, and how participation in the labor force has decreased over the past two decades (down by 2.7 million Americans as of June 2021). It is quite common to dismiss these as issues unrelated to racism, and instead to reduce these arguments to demands for "government handouts." The interesting thing about that claim, though, is that it doesn't stop there. Rather than address the inadequate and deficient systems that continue to punish those within the Black working class, we instead use so-called Christian ethics like "a person who does not work does not eat" to justify violent dehumanization. We should ask ourselves if people fighting for these changes and benefits are actually "lazy" or if they have been ill-positioned to survive and thrive as human beings in this deliberately constructed system.

Analysts like Nicholas Eberstadt in his significant book *Men Without Work: America's Invisible Crisis* have traced the problem faced by so many Black workers, but also by the entire American labor force, to the disappearance of unskilled work (at least the kind of jobs of that sort which still pay a living wage). Along with this reality has come increased work hours by those with jobs. The more hours worked by those employed, the fewer jobs are offered. Add to that the fluidity in the job market—few can count on working for the same company throughout a whole career. Additional pieces of the dynamic are the hiring biases and micro-aggressions that contribute to adverse personnel action, which is detrimental to professional development and progression. Consequently, some Black men seek alternative means of employment, including some which are sometimes considered illegal, instead of entering the job market (as defined by the US Department of Labor).

The job market has been just as frustrating for White men, who have stopped looking for work in larger numbers than Black men. So it's hard to say that Black men no longer seeking employment are any more culpable than everyone else who has given up.

Environmental Racism

Most people have heard about the contaminated water in Flint, Michigan, and how it severely impaired residents in that community. A 2017 joint report by the NAACP and the Clean Air Task Force found that Black residents are exposed to 38% more air pollution than White people, because they are 75% more likely to live near toxic pollution than the rest of the American population.[24] A 2021 study funded by the Environmental Protection Agency found the figure to be a 15% difference of pollution exposure between Black and White residents. A

---

24. Lesley Fleischman (CATF) and Marcus Franklin (NAACP), "Fumes Across the Fence-Line," Clean Air Task Force and NAACP, November 2017.

2019 study by researchers at the University of Washington and Stanford University found that Black people and poor people faced the highest risks of death from power plants' fine particle pollution.[25] This is no coincidence; this is a concerted effort by private businesses and city planners alike to create a dichotomy of experience in which the most vulnerable among us will bear the burden of our collective decisions. Even how society dumps garbage perpetuates racism.

Racism in our Educational System

It is tempting to turn to education of the impoverished and disadvantaged as the way out of these cycles. But the problems of racisms within our educational system are also more pervasive than many of us think. Public schools in economically advantaged communities are better resourced. From higher-quality school facilities to educators who are paid higher salaries, the disparity of academic investment and outcome creates a severe impact.

It's common to say that "those" schools have worse teachers. But as someone married to a former educator who taught in predominantly Black schools, Ellingsen can attest that labeling these schools "failing" is just as much a part of the problem as the lack of funding itself. Experienced teachers who make the extra effort to stay in these educational environments tend to have as great a passion—if not a greater passion—for

---

25. Maninder P.S. Thind, Chrisopher W. Tessum, Inês L. Azevedo, and Julian D. Marshall, "Fine Particulate Air Pollution from Electricity Generation in the US: Health Impacts by Race, Income, and Geography," *Environment Science Technology* (Nov. 20, 2019): pp. 1410–1419.

working with students in a particular disadvantaged community and for the teaching profession itself.

Woodall notes that a good example of how schools fail the poor and the Black student is provided by the life and story of Rev. Dr. Francys Johnson, a civil rights attorney and former president of the Georgia NAACP. As a student in a special education program in a rural public school system, Dr. Johnson was told countless times by administrators that he would not be able to go to college or pursue any of his dreams. Even the seminary with which we are both associated, the Interdenominational Theological Center, is served by distinguished faculty members who can tell parallel stories about the discrimination they endured in public schools because they were Black. They were advised by their White teachers to learn one of the skilled crafts, like painting or auto mechanics, or to learn how to type and do shorthand for a secretarial job, instead of entering academic scholarship and advanced research.

Sociologist Annette Lareau, in her book titled *Unequal Childhoods: Class, Race, and Family Life*, explains how our public education system fails these students. For instance, the public school system reflects a middle- and upper-class bias regarding parental engagement on behalf of their children. Because the Black community disproportionately faces poverty due to dynamics we discussed earlier, Black children receive less support from local police, public schools, and in some cases their own neighborhoods, with racist consequences. Schools have created an academic culture that makes it difficult for both poor parents and parents with less formal education to engage teachers and administrators. A culture or image has been created in which such parents may feel uneasy with teachers and principals, and the schedules for parental engagement rarely reflect sensitivity to the schedules of working parents. If our schools are going to avoid this kind of classism and racism we need reform that breaks down social and scheduling barriers, like the models we describe in chapter five.

There are other, perhaps more serious and overlooked, biases against Black and poor children in our educational system. Psychologists have observed that a significant number of impoverished children suffer pre-school childhood adversity. It begins in the womb, and in order to understand these dynamics we need an introduction to the hormone *oxytocin*. This hormone is produced in the hypothalamus (a section of the brain that manages hormones and coordinates the autonomic nervous system). Oxytocin then flows to the brain's pituitary gland and into the bloodstream. Its main function is in childbirth; it stimulates the contraction of the mother's uterus during labor. But it is secreted to other parts of the brain as well, and can be experienced by men as well as women. As such this hormone facilitates maternal behavior in women and paternal behavior in men. It plays a crucial role for a mother in the process of nursing her child. In facilitating bonding with the child, oxytocin inhibits fear and anxiety. It activates calmness in the nervous system and promotes sociality and social behavior. We'll have a lot more to say about these brain dynamics in later chapters.

On the other hand, in periods of sustained stress, hormones called *glucocorticoids* are secreted. This hormone is necessary to stimulate the fight-or-flight mentality you need when you encounter a stressful situation. But the hormone also impairs growth and tissue repair, a real problem for the fetus in the mother's womb. When the brain carries an excess of glucocorticoids during pregnancy, as in the case of a single mother in a poor neighborhood who is constantly worried about her family's next meal, it is likely to result in children with elevated levels of glucocorticoids themselves. Children born in these circumstances will in turn be energetic, even prone to hyperactivity. Maturation of the frontal cortex (the front part of the brain which regulates emotions and keeps our so-called animal instincts at bay) is delayed. This part of the brain is also essential to memory. It is likely that such a child will not then experience much oxytocin or the related hormone *dopamine*, both of which we'll see are essential to social skills and a sense of social responsibility. (Sociopaths are lacking or deprived of these brain chemicals.)

The child born in these circumstances faces not only these challenges in brain development from birth, but also the challenges of an impoverished environment, such as stress (worries about the next meal, a roof over the family's head), a lot of time without the attention of adults, and life in a tough neighborhood in which murder is a fact of life. These children are unlikely to enjoy experiences which can reverse these brain dynamics. (As we'll see, the human brain is plastic, which means it can always develop new brain connections which allow it to change, but this is less likely to happen in childhood when you're surrounded by the hopelessness of poverty or child abuse.)

And what does the American educational system do with these kids? It is biased against them, biased in favor of kids who've experienced lots of oxytocin and have a head start on the development of the prefrontal cortex and frontal lobe of their brains. We expect these children to sit still when it is hormonally difficult for them to do so, to exercise their underdeveloped frontal cortex in reading, arithmetic, and memory on a level with their more fortunate peers. And then we flunk them and chide them for their inability to obey and on account of their anti-social behavior. We put them in another situation of stress and effectively nurture all the undesirable brain developments happening to them at home. Since these characteristics can lead to sociopathic traits, this environment is another factor that increases the likelihood that children who grow up in impoverished communities will commit crimes. Public schools are indeed biased against the poor.

Now, these brain developments are racially neutral. But since, as we've noted, Black children are disproportionately represented in neighborhoods where this is likely to occur, these educational biases have racial dimensions. We're not giving up on the educational system, though, and we will offer some possible solutions to overcome this bias in chapter five. There are some inner city and rural schools serving impoverished communities that are already doing the work. You don't do it by lowering the bar for these kids. You do it by creating a community atmosphere in which their parents feel at ease in the school and with its personnel, and then you find ways to channel students' excess energy from their overdoses of glucocorticoids to activities which can facilitate making more neural connections with the front parts of the brain. But right now, the public school system is not the great equalizer we would like to say that it is. It's heavily biased against so many of our students, and thus our communities, and as such often fosters racism. That bias in turn is reflected in disciplines related to our educational system, including medicine.

Racism and Medicine

As with environmental racism, the impact that racism has on public health is extraordinary. Concentrating attention on the disparate health outcomes for people in Black communities has contributed to an increased awareness of what these realities are on any given day. Doctors are more inclined to under-estimate Black patients' pain and may hold back on offering some treatments under the assumption that Black patients lack adequate insurance coverage to pay for them.[26] Because of this, the most recent data published in 2018 by the Robert Wood Johnson Foundation reports that while the average life expec-tancy of a White person was 78.6, Black life expectancy was more than three years shorter.[27]

Even if we were to take a closer look at the impact of the coronavirus pandemic, about sixty-six per one hundred thou-sand Americans who died from COVID-19 were Black, while only 2.5 per one hundred thousand Americans who died were white. In part, this could be due to Black Americans being more susceptible to conditions such as diabetes and obesity, which makes individuals more at risk for COVID than oth-er categories. But another factor is that while 29.9% of whites hold jobs which allowed them to work from home during the pandemic, only 19.7% of African Americans were employed in such positions.[28]

Being victimized by racism leads to bad health outcomes, such as lower immune system effectiveness and tissue repair

---

26. See, for example, Janice A. Sabin, "How We Fail Black Patients in Pain," AAMC, January 6, 2020; Maryann Reid, "Why Going to the Doctor as a Black Person Is Hard," Forbes, February 10, 2020.

27. Schwandt, Janet Currie, et al., "Inequality in mortality between Black and White Americans by age, place, and cause and in com-parison to Europe, 1990 to 2018," *Proceedings of the National Academy of Sciences*, 2021: 118 (p. 40).

28. For this data, see Tiffany N. Ford, Sarah Reber, and Richard V. Reeves, "Race gaps in COVID-19 deaths are even bigger than they appear," Brookings Institute, June 16, 2020; and Elise Gould and Heidi Shierholz, "Not everybody can work from home," *Working Economics*, March 19, 2020.

efficacy, as well as lower life expectancy and higher levels of stress. It also seems that stress which people endure because of racism, no matter the size of injury or insult, is bad for health and longevity. These dynamics, it seems, relate to the length of human *telomeres* in the body. A telomere is a repeating sequence of double-stranded DNA at the end of a chromosome. The more frequently a cell divides, the shorter the telomeres become, wearing out the cell in the process. We age prematurely when the telomeres get shorter as cells keep dividing. This is a function of premature aging of the cells and early onset of disease, and is the result of stressors like discrimination, job loss, and the like.[29] No wonder Black life expectancy is considerably low, in comparison to that of whites'.

No two ways about it: being Black in America is not good for your health (and, as we have seen, it is not good for your housing, your pocketbook, or your peace of mind either). Why do we accept these conditions as normal? Indeed, too many (white) Americans are inclined to say, "Why can't people pull themselves up by their own bootstraps? Why are they looking for handouts? After all, America is a democracy." We will therefore conclude this chapter with relevant analysis of political representation and the related challenges which further maintain structural systems of racism.

Racism in American Democracy

As we began writing this book, the United States found itself at a tipping point—from an insurrection that took place at the

---

29. Arline T. Geronimus et al., "Race/Ethnicity, Poverty, Urban Stressors, and Telomere Length in a Detroit Community-Based Sample," *Journal of Health and Social Behavior* 56 (June 2015): pp. 199–234.

US Capitol, to nineteen state legislatures across the country enacting thirty-three voting rights bills that many argue are the most suppressive and restrictive the country has seen since Jim Crow. Rather than expand access to the ballot box, Republican-led efforts arguably were embracing strategies to curtail the progressive momentum in recent elections.

Disenfranchising formerly incarcerated people also remains a common strategy to bar people from the democratic process. In Florida, voters approved a referendum that would restore the voting rights of over a million formerly incarcerated persons, but the Republican legislature and governor have worked continuously to block them. These efforts to verify eligibility target Black voters, and this is clearly illustrated in the 2018 Georgia gubernatorial election. While only 32% of Georgia's population was Black at the time, 70% of voter registration applications put on hold by the Secretary of State were eligible Black voters. Nor can we forget gerrymandering efforts by some legislators that unlawfully move voters into district schemes that minimize the power of the electorate, particularly Black voters, and allow the legislators to maintain political power. Since the 1990s, one bipartisan strategy has been to redistrict Black elected officials into legislative districts populated by a White majority of the same partisan affiliation, or even to draw more White voters into predominantly Black districts, which ultimately dilutes their voting strength altogether.

At some point, we are going to have to blow the whistle on these dynamics and unjust practices. The history of America indicates that when you leave it up to local government and institutions—like universities, businesses, and Congress—to combat and ultimately end racism, it just won't happen. Note that not even simply increasing Black representation in these spaces will work, either. We need a much more comprehensive strategy that addresses the structural foundation of our society in order to make this right.

Cultural Dynamics

The ideologies of individualism and relativism which so dominate American thinking today further legitimize those who feel it necessary to maintain racial categories. Going back to at least the early twentieth century, if not before, American society bought into the relativistic worldview of German Enlightenment figures like Immanuel Kant (1724–1804). Kant and his followers maintained that a person is unable to reach an objective truth of a thing in itself or achieve a truth which transcends the individual's point of view.[30] In other words, we all have our own point of view of reality, and objectivity is impossible.

This way of looking at life has become the unquestioned creed of liberal scholarship in our educational institutions. It undergirds all the talk we hear from the academy about multiculturalism and Deconstruction. When religion has lost its credibility, this is what you get; but it does not stop there. It is also a core supposition of mass-media elites and business marketing techniques. But it is not the way that America's Founding Fathers—and leaders throughout much of the nation's first two centuries in existence—thought. They held a belief in common sense accessible to all.[31]

---

30. See Allan Bloom, *The Closing of the American Mind* (New York: Simon & Schuster, 1987), p. 141ff; Immanuel Kant, *Critique of Pure Reason* (1781), Int.; I.I; II.III.
31. See the philosopher of the Founders, Thomas Reid, *Essays On the Intellectual Powers of Man*, A. D. Woozley (London: Macmillan, 1941), pp. 364–365.

If we are unable to reason together, there is less hope of creating the kinds of coalitions it takes to improve the human condition. Perhaps the participation of non-Black people in the Movement for Black Lives is an indication that we are moving closer to transcending racism. In the meantime, the embedded-ness of this worldview in pop culture and in the academy needs to be addressed. Even the liberal ethos of our college faculty needs to consider if, in holding to these relativistic suppositions, their disciplines put up barriers to ending racism.

These dynamics are exacerbated by how they manifest in the development of American culture. Much has been written about rugged individualism in Western society. Many of the same racist elements present throughout human history that we touched on earlier can be found in what we discuss here.

Since the 1970s, when social commentator Christopher Lasch first noted these trends in his important book *The Culture of Narcissism*, American society has been increasingly characterized by a privatization of life, leading to an individualism gone mad. Americans have long been on a wild chase for self-fulfillment and pleasure. The old social norms that bound us and made us concerned about our social interactions and social relationships (family, the company, the town, life-long friends, religion), no longer function so effectively. The irony in the decline of religious faith and piety—particularly Christian faith—in favor of atheism or secular idolatry is that it has cost us a Trinitarian sense of the self. Without reference to a God who is constantly in relationship within himself (Father to Son to Spirit), we lose our sense of being made in God's image; thus, when we are not in relationship with others, we are not our most authentic and full selves. For to be in the image of a Trinitarian God means being in relationship with others. Without that awareness, each of us is left only with ourselves, a solitary individual seeking self-fulfillment and prosperity. The disconnect between this Christian vision of human life and how we live today is exacerbated by the realities of doing business in the globalized economy and by internet connectivity. Contrary to the lessons of globalization and internet connectivity, life is not all about how you feel about yourself and the admiration of others whom you use to feel good about yourself.

In this environment, therapeutic categories become the measure of happiness and health. Social scientists have described those born after the Baby Boomers in the twentieth century as Generation Me (see the book by Jean Twenge of that title). Consider how often we explain social ills in therapeutic categories, as consequences of poor self-esteem and self-image. American society has become narcissistic, encouraging people to become so preoccupied with the self that they have no sense of the worth of others except as objects or vehicles for their own self-fulfillment. For the narcissist, the things and people one encounters are, at best, mirrors of the individual, and when the reflection is *not* about the individual, the narcissist simply moves on. This ultimately aids in maintaining a racist society, since the narcissist feels no responsibility for anyone.

Those of us caught up in this sort of narcissistic ethos crave celebrity and admiration—not community. Unfortunately, this goal is empty and ignores all influences which might encourage people to consider the harmful impact such an aspiration has on other people, namely those in America's working, lower and middle classes. Save the desire for success and gratification, there remains only a stifling self-awareness of one's feelings of the moment. As for the impoverished and the minority members of the elite and upper classes, they too are subject to the yearnings and despair of this lifestyle. The media effectively markets its message to and for them. The harm in this mode of being is compounded by a socioeconomic and political system that effectively marginalizes the poor and minorities into the role of being an "other," effectively robbing them of even a glimmer of hope that they might achieve the desired model lifestyle that is routinely promulgated by the media.

To those who are Black, this model sends a message that mostly limits the human experience to a hope of being a celebrity, which makes being a "magical Negro"—a Black person who is considered an extraordinary talent, which tends to "absolve" them of or rescue them from the normal consequences of being Black—ultimately the only escape from this existential crisis. In a culture where people use other people to an end, there is even less likelihood that efforts will be made to eradicate poverty and ultimately racism. Indeed, keeping people "in their place" ensures an audience to envy the celebrity standard that all the "others" crave. Most aspects of the American way of life—from our laws, social procedures, and even medical systems—contribute to this condition of racism, thus impacting our collective ability to work for and achieve true justice for all.

Pulling It All Together

As we continue to engage the various sections of our society, it is extremely important to note that these elements of racism are neither isolated nor circumstantial. From the housing crisis, voter suppression, and failures of our public education system, to access to capital for small-business owners and federal unemployment programs, these circumstances have been designed intentionally for the benefit of a small few who seek to maximize profits. Without understanding the foundation of racism within our society, it is nearly impossible to understand *why* we are truly wired for racism as individuals. We are products of the environment around us and as such have been conditioned to believe that this situation is natural and God-inspired.

The first problem with racism is the concept of race itself, as it is not a legitimate biological category. Genetic research indicates that biological differences do not justify such distinctions, because there are scant genetic differences between racial groups. Francis Collins and the Human Genome Project established that all human beings are 99.9% similar in their DNA. In that case, where does the idea of distinct races have its roots? As Black columnist Ta-Nehisi Coates, wrote: "Race is the child of racism, not the father."[32] It is tempting to blame this concept on outdated science, but that is not the culprit. The modern concept of race emerged as a product of the colonial enterprises of European powers from the sixteenth to eighteenth centuries, when these powers identified race in terms of skin color and physical differences. This method of classification would have been confusing for people in the ancient world, since they did not categorize each other this way.

The epistemological moment where the modern concept of race was invented and rationalized lies somewhere between 1730 and 1790.[33] Europeans needed racial distinctions to justify why Africans could be enslaved. The conclusion: They are not like us Europeans. They are of a more "primitive race"

---

32. Ta-Nehisi Coates, *Between the World and Me* (New York: Spiegel & Grau, 2015), p. 7.
33. Nicholas Bancel, Thomas David, Dominic Thomas, eds., "Introduction," *The Invention of Race: Scientific and Popular Representations* (New York and London: Routledge, Taylor & Francis, 2014); see especially p. 11.

and so may be justifiably enslaved. Black people need saviors, they believed. In acknowledgement of the offensive nature of describing people in this category as "Blacks," there remains a pervasive attitude that is presented in the expectation that Black people have no ability to upset the perceived natural flow of White society.

From "stick to sports" to "separation of church and [politics]," the social and political agency of Black people is always called into question and made suspect due to their engagement within the public square. The participation of Black people in the media, politics, entertainment, and even in the academy has always only reflected a small segment of the thought and creativity of these institutions. Consequently, the narrative of White society's dominance and how it expects those in Black being (described further in the next section) to engage it remains in place. So how does society keep Black people "in their place"?

While media personalities such as Joy Reid, Van Jones, Bakari Sellers, Don Lemon, and Jemele Hill may be exceptions, the general response to Black people in these institutional positions of White society is often one of conditional acceptance and extrapolated tokenism. The gatekeeping of who—and what—is portrayed within the dominant narrative of society reflects a desire to maintain the racist standards that prop up the White society. Think of the dominance of whites in the media, modeling, classical art. To be sure there are some Black stars, but the hidden message is that they are exceptions.

The images of Black people shown throughout movies, broadcast news, social media, and other media as engaged in crime, lazy, and less intelligent, saturate the airwaves and continue to allow racist standards to manifest not only in Black minds but also Black being. We already know that it is a racist perception that Black people are more apt to engage in crime due to their Blackness alone.

There is also a standard perception within the White world which suggests that inherent within this Black being is a natural inability to contribute back to society. From claims of laziness and food stamp misuse to handouts and welfare, White society is convinced that Black people are a burden on society. Note that this does not account for the generations of public policy that have intentionally excluded Blacks from economic opportunity and sociopolitical advancement.

These realities constitute violence in ways which are not naturally included in such a definition, as the Black body is subjected to harmful conditions that it would not have been exposed to without the designation of being Black. This way of locating a place for Black existence in society means that African Americans are constantly pressured into both performance and productivity despite obvious deficiencies. And this status further compounds the dangers within the White structures of society for those who are Black.

Black Minds within White Society

The very fact that we have spent time here dispelling these widely propagated myths of Black abilities and behaviors has all sorts of consequences for everyday human life. If you haven't experienced this yourself, consider what your life might be like had you spent a lifetime knowing the world around you was both invested in and committed to maintaining structures that were created for your destruction. It is admittedly difficult for some readers to do, since the natural response to such a reality is to challenge these claims and suggest that either racism is a thing of the past, or that it is isolated to horrible people, but they themselves are not responsible—something we characterize as "White innocence."

Because so many people have been made to feel like "others" or outsiders, we return to the reality that the mind of a Black person is often in crisis. "To be conscious is to be in a forever state of rage," to paraphrase James Baldwin. There is always an examination or a test, and the standards for performance and production are higher for Black people. Some thrive within this competitive, self-testing ethos, as it is their inherent personality to be able to excel, but it's equally natural that some will quit, resign in despair, or rebel. This can even lead to some people never quite feeling at home in America (see the Toni Morrison quote to that effect in Andrew Hacker, *Two Nations*, pp. 38–39). The writer of Psalm 137 asks, "How can we sing the songs of Zion in a foreign land?"

Compounded with the vestiges of chattel slavery, Black Codes, and Jim Crow, a "new normal" in which Black being becomes synonymous with humility in the presence of White people develops. Such cultural and sociopolitical language communicates an inferiority that ensures a society of "law and order" which keeps you out of trouble. This creates a consciousness within the Black mind in which there is a natural response that rejects this condition. However, the continued suppression of this response leads to Black minds not only becoming confused and enraged, but also to Blacks feeling literally uncomfortable in their own skin.[34]

In addition, in our racist society the elites seek scapegoats for their failures. It is a way of making poor whites feel that the blame for their deteriorating conditions is not the fault

---

34. Isabel Wilkerson, *Caste: The Origins of Our Discontents* (New York: Random House, 2020), pp. 186–187, 290–291.

of the elites. Blacks and immigrants make good scapegoats for them (just as they have since Emancipation).[35]

These dynamics have implications for how "Black being" is experienced in a world of White structures. When we first examine this phrase, it may strike us as odd because we often refer to Blackness as race and identity—and rightly so. However, we need to recognize that racism and race *create* a separation of people according to the hue of their skin as well as a few other physical features. Racism is idolatrous because it makes these features absolute in determining a person's fate. Race has effectively become godlike as it presents the conditions of our destiny. The ones with perceived power—whites, in American society—take on godlike activities, ultimately determining the station and fate of the Black other.

We also previously observed that a kind of ontology, a sense of how the universe is structured and organized, has been created by racial distinctions. We cannot neglect the real consequences lying within this false concept, though. Blackness, functioning as an "ontological experience," ensures that human beings with a defined racial category of "Black" are forever chained to the very framework of society that was developed to enslave them. We recognize that certain elements of African heritage are present within the Black experience; however, this does not change the fact that ultimately, living as a member of a race (both Black and white) is largely a function of what society says you should be.

This indeed presents a challenge for us as we engage with racism in the mind because in acknowledgement of this truth, it creates a "crisis of consciousness" even for those within a specific racial category. For many, embracing this racial

---

35. Wilkerson, pp. 190–193.

identity as a logical response to systems of oppression is healing and liberative. But it must also be acknowledged that in many ways the creation of this identity was necessary for the development, success, and ultimately the sustaining of these sociopolitical institutions that we call "White society," too. Even the term "white" society is simply a certain designation upon the world in which we live, because "white," again, references an ontological disposition that embodies the oppressive realities that we are noting throughout this book.

This analysis makes clear that addressing racism is not merely a matter of addressing the anxiety we may feel when engaging members of another race. Overcoming racism cannot just be a matter of changing the natural biases in our brains, which we'll soon observe. Nor is it only a matter of how we engage people of different ethnic backgrounds. The systems that oppress must be changed, though as we will see, practicing faith and its impact on emotional maturity can aid in such a pursuit.

Racism seems to be systemic, even if it has its roots in certain dynamics of the human brain. It is time now to look at White guilt and protestations of innocence, which perhaps some readers may still be feeling. Once all readers, regardless of race, understand each other a little better, we might be ready to do what God and evolution have designed us to do: to work, live, and be free, together.

Chapter 2

The Ontology of Race:
White Innocence and the Black Other

As we begin a deeper dive, it is critical to acknowledge the very existence of the racial categories of Black and white. As a category, race creates an illusion of White innocence that is embedded within the very framework of American identity. It's a constant serenade of patriotic hubris that we sing to each other without end.

White innocence is the belief that it's those "others" who are racist. *They* are the ones who are responsible for this inequality. In the words of certain White Evangelicals, "It's those radical liberals who loot, riot, and want to defund the police. They are the racists." However, considering the data we've cited in the first chapter, we really know that refrain is a complete lie which has no basis.

Blackness as a racial classification inherently places those within said category in juxtaposition with those of illusorily innocent, White being—one being exclusively tied to the other. In a system of White supremacy, Black racial identity possesses an inherent basis of sociopolitical deficit in which the only natural alternative is to "embody a metaphysical nothing . . . , [which] serves as a destabilizing presence and force as well as that which whiteness defines itself against."[1]

---

1.   Calvin L. Warren, *Ontological Terror: Blackness, Nihilism, and Emancipation* (Durham, NC: Duke University Press, 2018).

It's the "pull yourself up by your own bootstraps" kind of mentality which the supposed White innocent enjoys when denying any real participation in racism and White supremacy; it's the "others" who are racist. Even if there are attempts to address historical deficiencies due to systemic racism, these efforts are usually met by the White innocents with legal challenges and claims of racial discrimination in which they become the oppressed victim. In their opinion, the Black others are responsible for this inequality.

The reality that we do not acknowledge is that the greatest threat to human existence is indeed racism. As racism manifests itself in human experience, White innocence—or the belief that White "beingness" is not responsible for the dehumanizing violence within White supremacy—creates illusions in which White people distance themselves from racism.

This is where the *ontology of race* becomes relevant. It is not just a useful concept for understanding racism at a deep level, but also for gaining insights about White innocence and Black protestations against critiques of institutional racism. As soon as Americans consider themselves to be white, they begin to participate in racism. According to the 2020 US Census, the very concept of being "white" estranges those who have "origins in any of the original peoples of Europe, the Middle East, or North Africa" from every other American. This definition effectively renders those who do not fit it different from the White majority. Those who are not classified as White are deemed as the "other" and inferior by those who consider themselves to be white. This inferior status of the "other" is regarded as the primary cause of all social ills or occasions of violence against those not belonging to the "select" White group.

Whenever there are violent exchanges in the human experience and Black people are subjected to dehumanizing realities, whites typically either categorically deny their individual involvement or reject the idea that an offense exists at all, never conceding that their status as White and alienation from the others is the cause of all the mess—and of their inability or unwillingness to see it. Why do whites sing that song? The obvious answer to our question is a five-letter word: GUILT, White guilt. That is *an* answer, but we need to examine its dynamics and note how it masks other, even more insidious, dynamics.

The dictionary reminds us that guilt is a painful feeling of self-reproach resulting from the belief that you have done something wrong. It is a tangled maze of emotions, but no matter, it does not feel good. We want to avoid it, if possible. And yet neurobiology tells us that guilt is intimately related to empathy, as both seem to stem from a part of the brain at its center termed the *deep limbic system*. It is the bonding and mood control center. This may explain some cases in which White Americans feel (or say they feel) no guilt about racism. You don't feel guilty if you don't empathize with the other. If I can't empathize with a member of the other race, I am not going to feel guilty about their plight. This explains why typically White people who have friends of another race are less inclined to be overt racists, why they will more likely concede White society's responsibility for injustices.

Of course, it's a long way from saying society is racist to admitting my own responsibility for racism, my own complicity in racism. "We didn't cause slavery," whites like to say; for African Americans, many want to forget slavery or not engage fully in taking on the system because it is working (at least for their immediate families). Why? Whites (especially liberals) want the approval of the sons and daughters of Africa in America. "It's the other (white) guys' fault, not mine," is what whites prefer to say (to others and to themselves).

One of the reasons for this retreat from reality on the part of whites and some Blacks is that the charge of America as a racist society feels like a threat to our system. Even if it is not deliberate or consciously done, a lot of us have been raised to see America as the Land of Opportunity. The sentiments of the Declaration of Independence echo in our "patriotic psyches" (even if we don't know the exact words very well): "We hold these truths to be self-evident, that all men are created equal, that they are endowed by their Creator with certain unalienable Rights, that among these are Life, Liberty, and the pursuit of Happiness." All of us have equal opportunity in this country—or so White Americans think. That's why we can't quite bear to think of the society to which we belong and we ourselves as racist. Some people, especially from other regions, are racist, but not America and not me (even if such sentiments depend on our repressing our guilt).

We need to keep the image of America as not inherently racist intact, we think, because the most vocal, if not the most committed, civil rights supporters have been believers in the government's role in solving the problem. However, when you turn to government to help solve your problems, you invest more and more in the professionals—politicians and the "experts" they hire—who administer the government apparatus. And, invested as they are in the system, they have less inclination to challenge what seems to be working, not to ask the tough questions about whether its programs might reflect inherent biases. One need only consider the marriage penalty built into the welfare system which penalizes stable two-parent-in-the-home poor families.

In addition, when you are looking for professionals to make decisions, an elitism is implied. And the whole concept of an "elite" has White overtones, for at least numerically and proportionately the professional in question is more likely to be White than Black. Consequently, when government and its programs intended to "help" the poor and oppressed are turned over to professionals, more often than not it is White bureaucrats making major decisions about the justice of the penal system for Blacks; about Black businesses, Black colleges and universities; about the welfare system; and more. Despite anyone's good intentions, the system seems to reflect White power. But whites do not want to concede that their support of such programs is supportive of the racism these institutions still prop up. To admit being racist themselves, even White liberals and progressives would have to begin challenging the things they've been doing for/to the Black community in a way few are brave and self-reflective enough to do. It would entail challenging the very things that they understand America to stand for.

Abdicating the administering of programs to heal our racial divide to professionals has other insalubrious consequences, especially for the poor and others who never had a real shot at reaching professional status. For one item, as famed columnist and commentator Thomas Frank has pointed out, professionals are heavily invested in the present system, not inclined to challenge it in the name of laboring or impoverished classes. This is what has happened to the leadership of the Democratic Party, Frank observed, and it is why organized labor and managed economic programs have not, since before the Clinton era, set the agenda in the party that once truly represented these concerns.[2]

Why? For one, it takes a major financial investment to get elected, and so governing bodies of American institutions,

---

2. Thomas Frank, *Listen, Liberal or, What Ever Happened To the Party of the People?* (New York: Metropolitan Books, 2016), especially pp. 30–31.

all the way up to the United States Congress, have incentive to appease the big donors. Frank demonstrates how Democratic candidates, no less than their competitors, have buddied up with Wall Street investors and then enabled legislation that has made life easier (and less regulated) for the Internet conglomerates of Silicon Valley.[3]

It becomes evident that it is nearly impossible to serve "the least of these" when the economic incentive is to continue to push policies that benefit the wealthy. The level of financial investment of the wealthy in political campaigns puts pressure on politicians to serve the interests of their investors.

America's founders were not unaware of these threats and seem to be allies for those of us seeking to change these dynamics. It is true that in *The Federalist Papers*, No. 35, Alexander Hamilton claimed that he did not believe we could mandate that all social classes be represented in Congress. But he was concerned that the interests of all classes be understood and attended to. And James Madison, in No. 57, insisted that elections ensure that legislators not just be drawn from the upper class. Famed twentieth-century theologian Reinhold Niebuhr issued an even firmer warning:

Government is never completely under the control of a total community. There is always some class, whether economic overlords or political bureaucrats, who may use the organs of government for their special advantages. Powerful classes dominate the administration of justice.[4]

The Founders' intentions aside, it is nevertheless the case that in its present form, one must question whether the system

---

3. Frank, pp. 128ff, 229ff.
4. Reinhold Niebuhr, *Moral Man In Immoral Society*, in Larry Rasmussen, ed., *Reinhold Niebuhr: Theologian of Public Life* (Philadelphia: Fortress Press, 1991), p. 58.

is rigged against Black people. It does not matter whether conservatives and Evangelicals are in power or whether power is held by progressives and liberals. The question is whether our very Constitutional system can offer opportunity for equality under the law. Many people, even White liberals who have bought into this system as it currently functions, remain both ignorant of systemic racism and psychologically committed to it. As a result, they are unable to admit its existence or take ownership of their own racism.

The foundational ideology associated with government professionalism and the institutions run by career politicos reflects and perpetuates racist biases in other ways. Many government professionals and the politicians who supervise them have bought into the ideal of a "meritocracy," a concept popularized by former Secretary of Labor Robert Reich during the Clinton Administration.[5] The concept certainly applies to Reich's old boss and to others in his administration, and can also be applied even to the Obama Administration.

Meritocracy seemed to be a reasonable explanation of their success, since many of those involved were not born into a bourgeoisie and/or politically elite class. They all attended and excelled academically at prestigious institutions, earning the credentials, respect, and higher economic mobility which usually accompany such an education. The system is therefore considered fair from the point of view of a professional elite. The danger with this view, however, is that proximity to power gained through this meritocracy is shrouded in ignorance of the powerless—and thus just perpetuates the illusion of White innocence. For those committed to the meritocracy, racism in the system is hard to fathom, for they see no harm done by

---

5.   Robert Reich, *The Work of Nations* (New York: Vintage, 1992).

telling people to "pull yourself up by your bootstraps" and ascribing failure to a lack of individual effort.

As we see time and time again, however, an unavoidable consequence of this meritocracy is also racism, as the expectation becomes that anyone can do the very same, since these opportunities are available to anyone and everyone. With this view of life firmly in place—not just among our politics and cultural gurus, but also in the media—racism and classist intolerance for the poor inevitably follow. Those who have not made it to the top have only themselves to blame. Thus, the poor and the imprisoned (who as we have noted are disproportionately Black) must be not as hardworking as those who have "made it," or may even be morally depraved.

Never mind, of course, that the poor, unless they get the break of some good mentors (which those from "the hood" who succeed in a meritocracy inevitably have had), do not have access to or know how to use the quality of educational opportunities the winners had. Never mind that many of the winners have had the kind of stability in their family home that allows for the maturation of their frontal cortex which allows intelligence to flourish instead of focusing on survival, while the poor kid from the same neighborhood grew up in an environment which impeded development of the frontal cortex (see chapter one for details). Some kids growing up in poverty (and again, note the disproportionate number of Black kids in these circumstances) never had a chance. Meritocracy and having folks who think they made it on their own administering our helping programs is inherently racist, or at least intolerant of the poor. Meanwhile the system and the perceptions of failure of those trapped in long-term generational poverty, many of whom are Black, just reinforce all the stereotypes that associate lower intellectual abilities and crime with African Americans.

Of course, the professionals can't see this. They can't consider themselves or the systems they administer racist, or else it would imply that the meritocracy does not exist. And they/we are not about to admit we have not deserved what we have. No wonder we like to say we're not racist, when we've gotten where we are through racist systems.

It is important here to make the point again that whiteness is not reducible to a simple racial category, but functions as a concept in a racist system that continues to dehumanize. Recall that the racist system has its own philosophical suppositions. We have noted that it posits an ontology—a set of concepts for structuring the universe. The major categories in this system are Black and white, with White designated as good and superior and Black as bad, evil, and "other." The darker someone or something is, the less White or good they are, as perceived by those caught up in the system. Recent scientific research conducted by New York University marketing professor Adam Alter and colleagues demonstrated that the majority of Americans associate Black with bad.[6]

In setting up this structure, this philosophical worldview ultimately removes God as the divine Creator and challenges the author of all things good. Race (especially for those who are categorized as white), not God, determines who we are in such a society. But the White working class, as Rev. Dr. Martin Luther King, Jr., would always remind us, should be just as committed to the same cause of racial

---

6. Adam L. Alter et al., "The 'Bad is Black' Effect: Why People Believe Evildoers Have Darker Skin Than Do-Gooders," *Personality & social psychology bulletin*, 42(12): pp. 1653–1665, November 17, 2016.

and economic justice as the American Negro because they too find themselves struggling amidst a period of great socioeconomic violence.[7]

Alas, most of the White working class did not and still does not heed Dr. King's advice. We certainly see this in the continuing support of Trump and Republican policies among the White working class. The pro-Republican votes cast by that group went as high as 62% in 2016 according to a Vanderbilt University study (though these numbers have eroded a bit since 2020, when Trump beat Biden barely 2 to 1 among this constituency). A recent correspondence between Ellingsen and the North American Lutheran Church (a predominantly White and theologically conservative denomination), for example, made it obvious that the church was unaware of how its policies are contrary to its membership's interests. Similarly, the NALC's 2021 May newsletter lectured against Black Lives Matter while these pastors and their middle-class parishioners keep losing economic ground.

Whites have their own reasons for defending the system while still insisting they are not racist (or else proudly proclaiming their racism). But this is even more anomalous given the fact that since the abolition of slavery in America, working-class whites have been and are in the same boat as African Americans. Yet they largely subscribe to the present system because it ensures that no matter how bad things are, they are not at the bottom. And since whites are considered to be at the top, the White working class maintains the (false) hope that maybe they can get there too. As economist Gunnar Myrdal has observed, poor whites hold to these convictions the fiercest and

---

7. Martin Luther King, Jr., *Stride Toward Freedom: The Montgomery Story* (New York: Harper & Row, 1958), Ch. 11.

so "are the people likely to stress aggressively that no Negro can ever attain the status of even the lowest white."[8]

No wonder there is so much overt racism among poor or working-class whites! They are fighting for their self-respect, for their "somebodiness." This fight becomes critical in understanding the human mind, as somebodiness depends on one's internal recognition of their own being. But in fact, to be fully human is to be involved in the mutual exchange of the divine experience in which two somebodies acknowledge the equal beingness. The distinct advantage of the poor or working-class White over a Black American is that the system is geared to whites feeling like somebodies and at the expense of Black citizens.

Even further, the capitalists and the politicians whom big money has bought have convinced working-class and poor whites that the hard times they are enduring are not the fault of the system, which is in fact rigged against them, but instead is the fault of all those "accommodations" made to Black and Brown people. This was especially the case in the rise of Trumpism. Language inserted in public discourse that claims to "save America" is really intended as a call to White salvation from the radical ideas of Black and Brown people. It is the dog whistle that is sounded by many ultra-conservative politicians seeking election on every possible level of government. Inherent within their thought process is a belief that Black being is a threat to their very existence—which it is not, unless their existence is predicated upon the very destruction of Black people.

In any case, these dynamics explain why some segments of the White poor and White working class are not even worried about whether they are racist or not. To be sure, like other whites in professional classes they may care about avoiding an

---

8. Gunnar Myrdal, *An American Dilemma*, Vol. 2 (London and New York: Routledge, 1944), p. 597.

image of being racist, at least when talking with certain kinds of churchgoers, professionals, or someone with a friend or relative who is Black. It is true, however, that most of the White working class do not worry about whether they receive any unjust perks for being White from the system. That blindness is precisely how the system masks the exploitation of the White working class, blinding them from an awareness that they are getting exploited alongside others and from realizing that challenging the system is not just to the benefit of Black people.

The illusion of White innocence has even infected parts of the Black community. Some segments of the various classes of Black elites are less likely to challenge the racist system and may be inclined to look negatively at those who have not experienced upward socioeconomic mobility and success—to instead associate them with crime and sloth (even though, as we've noted, many never had a meaningful chance).

In his book *The Audacity of Hope* (New York: Crown Publishers, 2006), Barack Obama explained why almost nobody is willing to concede he or she is a racist. "White guilt has largely exhausted itself," he writes (p. 247). Racial victimization is a tough sell, even among liberals. Unwillingness to claim you are a racist has to do with what you get from the systems in place and your own self-esteem. Robin DiAngelo is also correct in her recent book, *White Fragility: Why It's So Hard for White People to Talk about Racism*, which claims that part of the problem is the way we have been socialized; one aspect of that process is learning to define racism as the conscious, and unconscious, dislike of someone because of their race. It becomes even more dangerous when that [un]conscious hatred of another person is predicated upon disposition toward power. Then, to be accused of racism does not fit that hateful definition, and so we (both White and Black) instinctively deny the allegation. In modern American society we see ourselves as uniquely "exceptional," so we take offense when the accuser lumps us in with others.

Perhaps the deepest reasons for defensiveness are related to the perceived image of America as an equal-opportunity nation in which anyone who works and has talents can succeed—a view now supplemented by the idea of America as a meritocracy. Successful African Americans are also likely to embrace the system, at least insofar as they may also be inclined to blame the Black poor person or criminal for not "making it" like they have. In this system the humanity of the Black poor is challenged. For in a meritocracy, success is often a measure of one's humanity. The racism of this system also undermines the contributions of Black Americans, as their successes are not their own.

As voting rights advocate and founder of Fair Fight Action Stacey Abrams once wrote: "The myth of self-made success, or of bold action rewarded for its merits, may work in certain circles, but [Black people are] not often included in its penumbra. Self-made is a misnomer, a stand-in for a more complex narrative that includes the ability to work for no pay, to borrow from friends and family, to experiment and fail without falling too far."[9]

As we'll see when we consider the evolutionary way out of our racial mess, it is not to be expected that most of us will ever fail to give ourselves the credit we think we deserve. No wonder we don't want to be thought of, or see ourselves and our systems, as racist. There is another problem for whites faced with conceding they are racists because they profit from

---

9.   Stacey Abrams, *Minority Leader: How to Lead from the Outside and Make Real Change* (New York: Henry Holt, 2018), pp. 55–56.

a racist system. In his 2006 book *White Guilt: How Blacks and Whites Together Destroyed the Promise of the Civil Rights Era*, conservative Black commentator Shelby Steele claimed that if whites concede their racism and the racism of the systems they have dominated, they lose moral authority and with it their power and privilege. At least subconsciously sensing this, it is no wonder that whites and privileged Black professionals—as the members of Robert Woodson's 1776 Unites state in their book *Red, White, and Black*—do not want to concede to being racists or do not want to concede biases in the system. No one wants to renounce his or her power without some incentives.

Considering what is "in it for you," can you understand that if you think you are innocent and that racism is the other person's fault, there are a lot of reasons why you may be repressing the conclusion that you are responsible for the racial injustice in America? There are too many incentives for not drawing that conclusion, for wanting to plead innocent. The two of us, as authors and given our respective vocations (as a civil rights leader and as a White professor in a school of the Black Church), don't like admitting to it either. But insofar as we've both experienced much success, with Ellingsen's lighter Norwegian skin providing advantages that Woodall has not had, it's hard to admit these successes are the result of an unfair system. Maybe we don't really deserve the success we've had. Since we are not system elites, it's tempting to feel like we can blame the racist injustices on those with power; we're the good guys. But by laying this blame at their door we haven't succeeded in changing the system and we still even profit from its injustices. Surely, we could have done more. Can you make this confession with us, dear reader, that our innocence is an illusion?

What Makes Race Such a Big Deal?

Our analysis answers this question in part. The big deal about race has to do with sociology, politics, power, and faith—not biology. And it's the first three of these issues that are the real cause of White fragility, the unwillingness to take responsibility for racism and do something about it. We will also see, though, in the next chapter, that *racism* has to do with biology, with brain dynamics. But it is not biology that really divides us, and it certainly does not have to.

Before moving to the next chapter and assessing the way in which our brains make us racist, we close this chapter with a reminder that the idea of race is not a significant biological differentiator, for the concept has political and social origins. Genetic research has demonstrated that there are scant genetic differences between Blacks and whites, indeed between all the races. But racial differences could be used to justify the enslavement of Africans, so the conclusion was drawn: They are not like us Europeans. They are of a more "primitive race" and so may be justifiably enslaved. Blacks need caretakers, saviors.

This idea of the inherent inferiority of Blacks continues to pollute much dialogue surrounding race, but biology does not justify its existence. The analysis of neurobiological dynamics which follows is strictly speaking about observations concerning how the brain works when encountering those of a different appearance and/or background. It has nothing to do with showing that on a strictly biological basis the brain necessarily distinguishes one race from another. Indeed, genetic comparisons reveal that the differences between those of African and European ethnic origins are few and minor. Let's get to the next chapter now to identify how biology demonstrates that we really are all inclined to racism.

Chapter 3
Lessons from Neurobiology

As we've already suggested, exciting research in the field of neurobiology is providing some insightful clues about racism. The data also indicate how and why we are all inclined toward racism, and how we indeed practice it in our everyday engagements. When talking about the brain and its development, we need to think from back to front. That's the way it develops, and the way it evolved in *Homo sapiens*. Let's begin with how the brain functions.

Genes are the informational building blocks of the human brain, making possible the one hundred billion *neurons* (nerve cells) which comprise this three-pound organ of wrinkled tissue serving as the seat of the mind. The neurons themselves consist of cell bodies and several fibers clothed by and interconnected with grayish nerve tissue called *gray matter*. These cells carry information and can transmit electrical currents, which are the agents of this communication.

Unlike other cells of the human body, neurons include thread-like extensions of themselves or fibers of neurons called *dendrites*, which carry these currents. Dendrites generate and transmit electrical currents to neurons when they receive electrical pulses from other neurons. The interconnections between neurons in the gray matter enable the brain to interpret signals from sense organs, compare them with memories, and plan suitable action.

Communication between entities is one thing. Physical interconnections like neurons make are something distinct from mere communication. Something new is created. This process also includes the general nerve fibers called *White matter*, which connect the brain's cortex (its outer portion) to the rest of the human nervous system, enhancing communication of the brain with the entire body. But within the brain itself, not all its neurons are interconnected. This is a blessing, for if they were, the possibility of forging new neural connections (and so enabling the transmission of new knowledge) would be impossible. On the contrary, new connections are always being formed in the healthy and active human brain. In that sense, we can speak of the brain as being self-organized.

The brain is also assisted in building these neural connections by certain brain chemicals called *monoamine neurotransmitters*, which are triggered by the electrical impulses caused by neural dendrites , and which ferry signals from one neuron to another that in turn facilitate the binding of these neurons. And when these chemicals provide pleasure (as in the case of one we've already noted, the amphetamine-like chemical dopamine), the connections formed between neurons are reinforced and likely to be retained.

Another hormone we have discussed, oxytocin, also acts as a neurotransmitter. It not only affects muscle contractibility to facilitate sperm and egg transport, but it also increases feelings such as love and empathy as it calms the brain and makes one want to cuddle with the object of one's affection. Both oxytocin and dopamine are often labeled the brain chemicals of love and sociality.

When these transmitters are functioning efficiently, all parts of the brain are rewarded. The real action takes place in the *frontal lobe*, the last part of the human brain to develop. As this part of your brain becomes active, you are more likely to concentrate on a task or object. Then you will not let your immediate passions or your auditory, spatial, pain, or temporal sensations dominate; the brain is more likely to produce oxytocin and dopamine, inducing experiences of pleasure.

When you attempt to locate yourself in space and time, focusing on physical appearances or physical objects, location, or proximity to others, the *parietal lobe*, in the upper back of your brain, is activated. It is one of the oldest parts of the brain, and we share much of it in common with all animals. But when it is activated, the same pleasurable feelings are not experienced as when the frontal cortex and its prefrontal lobe are in operation. In other words, you get more pleasure from front-brain activities—like concentration on a project, lovemaking, or social engagement—than you do from just moving your body, looking at the size of a room and noting its colors, or just observing who's in the room with you. Of course, if there is an attraction or intimate attachment to others who are in the room, touching or concentrating on them will activate the frontal cortex, inducing the "good feeling" chemicals.

What does all this background on the human brain have to do with racism and denying it? Let's see.

Racism in the Brain

A number of neurobiologists and psychologists have analyzed how the brain functions in racism or contributes to racist behaviors.[1] Much of this research has focused on the amygdala (a

---

1.   See, for example, Eberhardt; E. A. Phelps et al., "Performance on indirect measures of race evaluation predicts amygdala activation," Journal of Cognitive Neuroscience 12(5) (2000): pp. 729–738; Adam M. Chekroud et al., "A review of neuroimaging studies of race-related prejudice: does amygdala response reflect threat?", Frontiers in Human Neuroscience 8 (2014).

component of the limbic system in the brain), and it has been conducted since as early as the 1960s.[2]

The limbic system is a set of structures in the front of the brain. It is immediately behind the temporal lobe, but still in the forebrain. It supports a variety of functions, including emotion, behavior, motivation, long-term memory, and sense of smell. This part of the brain seems responsible for the fight-or-flight response to threats or new experience typical of many animals, and certainly of human beings.

The amygdala is part of this system, playing an important role in emotion and behavior, especially in the processing of fear. Brain research has indicated that the amygdala is in fact involved in race-related evaluative processing.[3] Other studies found that whites with the most negative attitudes toward Blacks exhibited the greatest differences in amygdala activity when viewing Black faces, as opposed to White faces.[4] Similarly, in 2005, Mary Wheeler and Susan Fiske found that those studying photographs of White and Black faces had greater amygdala activity when studying Black faces than when considering White faces.[5] On the other hand, in one 2013 study led by Aleksandr V. Shkurko, such greater amygdala activity was not observed consistently related to racial in-group/out-group

2.   Donald T. Campbell, "Stereotypes and the perception of group differences," *American Psychology* 22 (1967): pp. 817–829.
3.   See Phelps et al.
4.   John McConahay, in John D. Dovidio and Samuel L. Gaertner, eds., *Prejudice, discrimination, and racism* (Cambridge, MA: Academic Press, 1986), pp. 91–125.
5.   Mary E. Wheeler and Susan T. Fiske, "Controlling Racial Prejudice: Social-Cognitive Goals Affect Amygdala and Stereotype Activation," *Psychological Science* 16 (2004): pp. 56–63.

responses.[6] However, that study measured not just race-related reactions but also involved age and gender comparisons.

Indeed, not all amygdala activity is problematic. It seems that heroes and very altruistic people have more amygdala activity than sociopaths, but in their brains it is coupled with higher levels of empathy than for most of us.[7]

There seems little doubt that amygdala activity more typically distinguishes between in-group and out-group in its reactions.[8] Other research which seems to confirm these findings is a 2004 study by William A. Cunningham, M. K. Johnson, J. D. Gore, et al. Cunningham and his colleagues found that less prejudiced individuals show less amygdala activity when viewing the out-group. The implications of these findings say quite a bit about the seeds of racism. If the amygdala processes fear and puts you in a fight-or-flight mindset, then the more it is stimulated the more fearful and hostile you're likely to be.[9]

Well, it seems that when a person is confronted with Black (male) faces, whites are likely to be on edge, to be ready to fight (more prone to violence, like White police who have pulled the trigger on Black men, or lynch mobs) or to flee (they'd rather not socialize or work with Black people). At the very least, when a

6. Aleksandr V. Shkurko, "Is social categorization based on relational in-group/out-group opposition? A meta-analysis," *Social Cognitive and Affective Neuroscience* 8: pp. 870–877.

7. Abigail Marsh, reported in "60 Minutes," Nov. 7, 2021.

8. See Allen J. Hart et al., "Differential response in the human amygdala to racial outgroup vs. ingroup face stimuli," *Neuroreport* 11 (2000): pp. 2351–2355; Phelps et al., "Performance on indirect measures of race evaluation."

9. William A. Cunningham et al., "Separable neural components in the processing of black and White faces," *Psychological Science* 15 (2004): pp. 806–813.

person engages with a member of another racial category he or she tends to be more uptight and/or on edge. And these brain dynamics would seem to pertain to African Americans in their engagement with whites. In that sense, we are all racially biased. Unless the frontal lobe of our brain takes control, and as long as society teaches us suspicion toward others, we are not naturally inclined to treat people equally (or at least we're prone to treat a member of another race differently).[10] According to the science, whites' denials of their racism are lies! The predisposition for Black people to have negative attitudes towards whites could arguably be a biological reaction in response to the systemic forces of racial violence. It is indeed quite difficult to call members of an oppressed racial group "racist," as by definition racism is about power and control—not feelings.

Of course, these observations need to be qualified, and we'll do more of that throughout the remainder of the book. A related study indicates embedded prejudice, taking the form of whites sometimes claiming all Blacks look the same (and Black people have been known to say the same about White people). One 2007 study revealed that White Americans remember White faces better than Black ones. Viewing the face of a different race seems to depress the functioning of the cortical region

---

10. It is true that recent research has found that the amygdalae of young children are not as sensitive to race as those of adolescents; see Eva Telzer et al., "Amygdala Sensitivity to Race Is not Present in Childhood but Emerges over Adolescence," *Journal of Cognitive Neuroscience* 25 (2) (October 15, 2012): pp. 234–244. But it is also widely recognized that in the case of children born and raised in non-threatening environments, amygdala connectivity and fear of all realities encountered is much less developed than it is in adults. See Elina Thomas et al., "Newborn Amygdala Connectivity and Early Emerging Fear," *Developmental Cognitive Neuroscience* 37 (June 2019).

of the brain that specializes in facial recognition.[11] Our brains seem to shut down when we have opportunities to observe the physically nuanced expressions of members of other races.

Other disturbing habits of our brains regarding race should be noted. Regarding the stimulation of the amygdala and the fear which its activation processes, in a 1998 study conducted by Anthony G. Greenwald and colleagues it was found that White subjects had more startled eye blinks to Black faces than to White faces.[12] This eye blinking observation could have implications for interpreting our failure to recognize details of faces of members of other races. In addition, researchers have found that when we encounter threatening stimuli, we tend to selectively give our attention, focusing on what is threatening. Images of Black faces caught the selective attention of White test subjects more than images of White faces did.[13] Is this not evidence that subliminally, at least, we view each other as threats? That's also related to the amygdala activity that looking at or being with members of another race seems to heighten.

These findings need to be interpreted, considering what we have already observed about fear we have of each other being related to what we already think of each other, and so racism is

---

11. Alexandra J. Golby et al., "Differential Responses in the Fusiform Region to Same-Race and Other-Race Faces," *Nature Neuroscience* 4 (2001): pp. 845–850.

12. Anthony G. Greenwald, Debra E. McGhree, and Jordan L. Schwartz, "Measuring individual differences in implicit cognition: The implicit association test," *Journal of Personality and Social Psychology* 74 (1998): pp. 1464–1480.

13. Sophie Trawalter et al., "Attending to Threat: Race-Based Patterns of Selective Attention," *Journal of Experimental Social Psychology* 44 (2009): pp. 1322–1327.

not just rooted in neural/psychological processes. A 1989 study by Patricia G. Devine found that amygdala reaction by whites to Black faces varied to the extent that the White subjects' attitudes reflected negative stereotypes of African Americans.[14] That does not negate that overall, human beings instinctively tend to react with fear to encounters with another race, but it does show that this fear is at least in part conditioned.

Another related piece of data has to do with how the fear we already feel from the other is heightened by whether the other is gazing directly at us. A 2008 study led by Jennifer Richeson and colleagues found that amygdala activity in whites in reaction to Black faces was heightened when the Black person had a direct gaze at the White subject.[15] Until we turn things around, that might be another valuable lesson for Black parents who feel it is necessary to give "the talk" about racism and police officers to their children. It also highlights how scientific research displays the double standards White people seem instinctively to have in engaging African Americans.

Other data indicates the uptightness, our activated amygdalae, that we seem to experience when engaging members of another race. B. Keith Payne demonstrated that implicit racial prejudices (as determined by a device called the Implicit Association Test) are more likely expressed in

---

14. Patricia G. Devine, "Stereotypes and prejudice: Their automatic and controlled components," *Journal of Personality and Social Psychology* 56(1) (1989): pp. 5–18.

15. Jennifer A. Richeson et al., "Eye-Gaze Direction Modulates Race-Related Amygdala Activity," *Group Processes & Intergroup Relations* 11 (2008): pp. 233–246. See also Trawalter et al., "Attending to Threat."

behavior by people with poor executive control.[16] This observation seems to make clear that in avoiding racist behaviors,
our frontal lobe must exercise control over the "animal" instincts of the amygdala for us to behave civilly. We seem to be
programmed by the oldest parts of our brains to racism, or
rather to be innately fearful (at least on guard) with those who
do not look like us or who do not "belong" with us.

Studies also indicate that amygdala activity associated
with racism—either perpetuating or receiving it—is bad for
your health. The American Psychological Association reported
that "common and pervasive exposure to racism and discrimination" creates a "daily stressor" for Black people.[17] Increases
in stress cause elevated levels of cortisol in the body, which
can lead to cardiovascular disease.[18] Likewise, both racists and
those victimized by racism release lower levels of the hormone
DHEA-S, which repairs tissue damage.[19]

By contrast, when the frontal cortex is inert (instead of
controlling the amygdala and its role in racial fear), we lose
out on our brains getting saturated with oxytocin and dopamine, which enhance happiness and strengthen the immune
system.[20] Exercise of the prefrontal cortex (the executive

---

16. B. Keith Payne, "Conceptualizing Control in Social Cognition:
    How Executive Functioning Modulates the Expression of Auto-
    matic Stereotyping," *Journal of Personality and Social Psychology*
    89 (2005): pp. 488–503.
17. "Physiological & Psychological Impact of Racism and Discrimina-
    tion for African Americans" (2013).
18. Sarah Zhang, "The Physical Damage Racism Inflicts on Your Brain
    and Body" (2016), *Science* 87.12.
19. Elizabeth Page-Gould, "Warning: Racism Is Bad for Your Health,"
    Mind & Body (2021).
20. Tong Li et al., "Approaches Mediating Oxytocin Regulation of the
    Immune System," *Frontiers in Immunology* (7) (2017): p. 693.

functions of the brain) may be enhanced for Black people with whites, and this can benefit their pleasure in the encounter. In a 2005 study, J. Nicole Shelton and her colleagues observed that African Americans who are primed to think about racial prejudice and then have an interaction with White people tended to engage and enjoy the conversations with the White partner with even more intimacy, smiles, and shared dialogue than with another African American.[21]

The data indicate that given the fear and emotions stirred in our brains by engagement with other races, we are not currently spontaneously inclined to treat members of other races civilly. Avoiding our embedded racist propensities calls for some work. Does it have to be so hard? Maybe "all we need is love" among us. Maybe we just need a pill which can better control the amygdala or calm us down. Researchers at Oxford University have found that the genetic drug propranolol could remove immediate racial bias; chill us out a little, so to speak.[22] But there is no indication that a pill or any merely biological intervention changes racial attitudes. Even love and its associated brain chemicals won't solve all our racial injustices, it seems.

Even Oxytocin and Love Are Ethnocentric

Neurobiologists have even unraveled how the way we love can contribute to racial prejudice. Recall that oxytocin is the neurochemical which not only facilitates the nursing and nurtur-

21. J. Nicole Shelton, Jennifer A. Richardson, and Jennifer Salvatore, "Expecting to Be the Target of Prejudice: Implications for Interethnic Interactions," *Personality and Social Psychology* 31(2005): pp. 1189–1202.

22. Sylvia Terbeck et al., "Propranolol reduces implicit negative racial bias," *Psychopharmacology* 222 (2012): pp. 419–424.

ing process with young children, but also disposes those whose brains are saturated with it to be more compassionate—not just to children but to all our fellow human beings. Could this be a potential biological key to overcoming racism? Both the major religions of the world and most of the great humanist options prescribe love for overcoming racism and hate. But it is not a complete answer on its own, it seems, at least not naturally.

Research undertaken in the Netherlands, where polls indicate that there are significant prejudices against Germans and Muslims, describes the impact on several Dutch men who were given injections of oxytocin or placebo. The men remained just as inclined to attribute negative characteristics to Germans and Muslims as they were prior to experiencing oxytocin in higher levels.[23] This is a logical observation, since what oxytocin does is to bind us to our children who bear our genes or to the lover with whom in intimacy we created this child with whom we now share genes.

Other studies have shown that the love motivated by the other brain chemical of sociality, dopamine, is also selfish. A 2007 study led by William T. Harbaugh demonstrated that people who are most generous are more inclined to dopaminergic activation and as a result give more.[24] This makes sense insofar as dopamine is a chemical of pleasure; therefore, when you love and do and sociable things you are also rewarded by getting more of it.

These are interesting observations because they suggest that our human behaviors are normalized through self-interest.

---

23. Carsten K. W. De Dreu et al., "Oxytocin promotes human ethnocentrism," *Proceedings of the National Academy of Sciences* 108 (2011): pp. 1262–1266.

24. See Robert Sapolsky, *Behave: The Biology of Humans at Our Best and Worst* (New York: Penguin, 2017), pp. 548–550.

Of course, Christians have been saying that for centuries, identifying sinful dimensions in human nature which biologists seem likely to confirm. Biologists speak of our "selfish genes" and Christians call it concupiscence, believing that such selfishness permeates all that we do because of sin (see, for example, Romans 7:14–23).[25] There are also opposing thoughts within the Christian faith about the nature of the human condition. Of course an alternative, then, in Christianity is to stress the natural innocence of the human condition. This may lead to dissatisfaction with racism and the desire for the human community to overcome it. That is why there is such a great push to organize communities, to help us see our fellow human being as a neighbor, a friend, instead of a random stranger.

Likewise, even when you do the selfless deed, it feels good, right? Now we know why. When we are loving, we are rewarded by the good-feeling chemicals flowing in our brains. But this is not love, which would spontaneously lead us to meet the needs of those of other ethnicities whether or not we sense that they (the "other") are part of us. More on that in the final chapters.

What We Learn from Neurobiology

The scientific research findings take away the protest that "I am not a racist." The neurobiology of the brain functions in ways that predispose us to racist attitudes toward the other, precisely because we are on guard with members of communities to which we do not belong. The amygdala in our brains (and all the uptightness that goes with it) is a lot more active

---

25. Richard Dawkins, *The Selfish Gene* (Oxford University Press, 1976); Augustine, *On Man's Perfection in Righteousness* (415), XIII.31.

in these encounters than we usually experience in our own community. We relate to members of other communities differently than how we relate to those in our own community.

Of course, we are always more anxious around those who are not part of "us," not part of the family or our closest circle of friends. But the amygdala seems to work harder in rooms filled with a significant number of members of another race than it does when you are in the presence of people of the same skin color as you. You just don't want to do dumb things in front of them, say something stupid. You may even feel left out of some of the cultural cues, like you feel whenever you're in new territory (whether it be another part of the country, another company, or with a group where the majority has a different nationality than you). Neurobiology teaches us that these experiences are not unique to individuals, or just to one race. We need to be on guard, because it is precisely what we do with these feelings and experiences that makes us racist and leads to the situation we are in.

After you get to know the people of the different ethnicity in a room—really get to know them well—then some of the panic you felt in that room with the group different from you gradually eases, until it just feels like it does when you are in a room where your race is in the majority. There's even scientific verification for this dynamic. A 2012 study led by Kevin Bickart of Boston University and colleagues found that there is a relationship between the size of one's social network and the way in which the amygdala is connected to the rest of the brain.[26] If you have a large and complex social network, you will likely not be as victimized by fear and

---

26. Kevin C. Bickart et al., "Intrinsic Amygdala-Cortical Functional Connectivity Predicts Social Network Size in Humans," *The Journal of Neuroscience* 32 (2012): pp. 14729–14741.

may better be able to handle it and your racist propensities. If your network is broad, you know people of other races, and then people of another race are not so much "the other." They are part of "us."[27] Building such relationships keeps the amygdala in check in our inter-racial relationships.

These dynamics are indeed the same for Black and white. Yet there is a significant difference. Racial biases and unease become racism when those with more power act on these biases. As we will see in the next chapter (and as we saw in chapter one), in the United States and in most of its institutions, whites exercise a disproportionate type and level of power. Consequently, their prejudice has real impact on the lives of human beings. These racist biases can, and historically have, cost Black people economic opportunities, social mobility, livelihood, liberty, and/or their very lives. African Americans don't collectively hold that kind of socioeconomic power to impact the communal condition of "those whites," though in principle they could function in biased ways in their own businesses and institutions.

We all face challenges when relating to each other as fellow human beings. This idea of implicit bias rooted in the brain is woefully insufficient if we stop there. Its critics are correct that it can be used by whites as an easy way out of their responsibility, claiming that since everyone has these biases, and we can't fully control them, racism is not their fault. Don't read what we've written here that way. The next chapter will take away this easy way out. Keep in mind that the imbalance of power in America means that White people need to take

---

27. Melissa J. Williams and Jennifer L. Eberhardt, "Biological Conceptions of Race and the Motivation to Cross Racial Boundaries," *Journal of Personality and Social Psychology* 94(6) (2008): pp. 1033–1047.

responsibility for acting on and correcting the discomfort they have with Black people.

Scientific data supports this concern as well. A 2013 research project led by Aleksandr V. Shkurko found that amygdala responses to Black faces are the same for whites as Blacks.[28] In a society which demonizes Black men, portraying them as violent and angry, this racist image has even seeped into the consciousness of Black minds. This is another reason why we cannot just stop with biology in our study of racism. Biology does not explain how American life can impose such negative images on Black people about themselves to the point that they don't even trust each other.

The findings of this chapter make it clearer that "White innocence" is a myth. We are all inclined to racist bias. Now what to do about it? We can address the inclinations of our brain through faith and other front-brain activities, but racism is not just the dislike of people because of their race. It is also not just the implicit bias against or anxiety we feel when encountering members of other races. With neurobiological insights we've gained in this chapter we will see the sociology, economics, and politics a little differently. We can now recognize that the racist systems and laws analyzed in chapter one are really expressions of and seem to be the result of our discomfort with those who are different from us. But we still need the insights of all of these disciplines to help us understand how to implement in practice the scientific data to understand and challenge America's original sin—its racist idolatry.

---

28. Shkurko, pp. 870–877.

How Evolution and Religion Challenge Race Idolatry and Make Us More Human

The field of evolutionary theory and a sub-discipline, the evolution of religion, have some exciting insights for addressing our racial animosities and injustices. As the chapter title suggests, these disciplines teach us that in challenging racism it may come down to something as simple as needing to be more human. Given the less-than-overwhelming abilities humans have in comparison to most animals, though (such as physical strength and speed, fierce fangs to defend against predators or to capture prey, or even the innate ability to discern and escape danger), it is intriguing that humans have dominated the ecological order, exercising control over most living things. The size of the human brain has been noted as a possible explanation for this dominance. Modern evolutionary theory has developed sophisticated observations about the dominance of *Homo sapiens* within the animal kingdom and about the size of our brains which can provide keys to dealing with racism and perhaps solving a lot of our other human problems.

Cooperation Is the Name of the Game

Evolution teaches us that the behavior of all creatures is a function of natural selection. To understand the human species, you need to recognize its relation to its ancestral environment.

Throughout recorded history and even in prehistoric times we have always been surrounded either by other *Homo sapiens* or by hominoid predecessors. Evidence suggests that in order to account for all the genetic variants in *Homo sapiens*, given mutation rates and the length of *Homo sapiens'* existence (at most two hundred thousand years), we must have evolved from a population of seven thousand in Africa.[1]

In short, human beings have always been in community with other human beings! Since early *Homo sapiens* were themselves enmeshed in a community, we can assume that throughout our evolutionary history we have been hanging out with other cooperative people in close-knit groups.[2] We are a cooperative species evolving from cooperative forebears! This insight is borne out by archaeology and genetic biology. It is a finding which can help account for the size of human brains, for the larger brains we have are functions of the more fully developed frontal lobes *Homo sapiens* have developed, which control our animal instincts and selfishness. Albert Einstein, himself an enemy of racism, understood physics to include our cooperative nature. He once wrote:

A human being is a part of the whole, called by us "Universe," a part limited in time and space. He experiences himself, his thoughts, and feelings as something separate from the rest—a kind of optical delusion of his consciousness. The striving to free oneself from this delusion is the one issue of true

---

1.   Albert Tenesa, Paul Navarro, et al., "Recent Human Effective Population Size Estimated from Linkage Disequilibrium," *Gennome Research* 17, No.4 (2007): pp. 520–526.

2.   David Sloan Wilson, *This View of Life: Completing the Darwinian Revolution* (New York: Vintage, 2020), pp.151–153.

religion. Not to nourish it but to try to overcome it is the way to reach the attainable measure of peace of mind.[3]

We'll return later to this point about the role Einstein thinks religion plays in prodding us to become more human by widening our circle of compassion to embrace all living creatures. To be sure, other species do cooperate. Birds, bees, and many mammals do, for example. However, much animal cooperation is a function of sharing a common gene pool. Though perhaps not at the earliest stages of human evolution, modern *Homo sapiens* are unique in their ability to cooperate in large communities, even among those who do not share many common genes.[4]

Consider how much driving on highways and streets involves cooperation and how much happens in a big business or a nation, the globalized forms of economic collaboration! *Homo sapiens'* ability to cooperate truly is amazing. John Paul II spoke of the social love and solidarity among human beings. Black Evangelical theologian Jemar Tisby claims that our solidarity is a function of the fact that we are all made in the image of God.[5] But alas, though we have been created in this way, the realities of racism make clear that we often do not

---

3.　Albert Einstein, letter, Feb. 12, 1950; see Fred Jerome and Rodger Taylor, *Einstein on Race and Racism* (New Brunswick, NJ: Rutgers University Press, 2006).

4.　Yuval Noah Harari, *Sapiens: A Brief History of Humankind* (New York: Harper Collins, 2015); Matt Rossano, *Supernatural Selection: How Religion Evolved* (Oxford University Press, 2010), especially pp. 40–41; Robert Sapolsky, *Behave: The Biology of Humans at Our Best and Worst* (New York: Penguin, 2017), especially pp. 372–373.

5.　John Paul II, *Redemptor hominis* (1979), 32–33; Jemar Tisby, *How to Fight Racism: Courageous Christianity and the Fight Toward Racial Justice* (Grand Rapids, MI: Zondervan, 2021), p. 9.

act according to our innately cooperative natures. Christians, Jews, and Muslims call this sin.

Dietrich Bonhoeffer, a theologian who was martyred in the struggle against Adolf Hitler, also offers relevant observations. He contended that human beings are a synthesis of act and being, individual but the result of engagements with others.[6] This insight reminds us of the old African adage: It takes a village to raise a child. We are all in this thing called life or human society together.

This insight has profound implications for our struggles with racism. If what makes us human is our ability to cooperate in large communities and across genetic lines, then racism—or at the very least giving in to our fears stimulated by an active amygdala during cross-racial encounters—truly makes us less human. The very presence of racial categories, again, commands us to be less human as we recognize each other less as neighbors and friends but more as one or the "other." If we want to practice and affirm our collective humanity, we need to eliminate racial distinctions by building community through the struggle for equity and justice.

This commitment requires that we make space for the voices and stories of people who are most impacted by and are closest to the oppression. Resolving to simply have "community conversations" and pushing diversity and inclusion initiatives without centering the lives, voices, and experiences of those most impacted and marginalized by these racist realities is at best performative and at worst violently traumatizing. As Indian activist and scholar Arundhati Roy so eloquently puts it, "There is really no such thing as

6.   Dietrich Bonhoeffer, *Act and Being*, ed. and trans. Hans-Richard Reuter (Minneapolis: Fortress Press, 2009), p.130.

the 'voiceless.' There are only the deliberately silenced, or the preferably unheard." A lot of modern liberation theology makes this point as well.[7]

We encourage allies to join in the struggle, even if taking a stand will be socially difficult, uncomfortable, or even require self-sacrifice. This is not a new insight, however. Rev. Dr. Martin Luther King, Jr., effectively operated with this idea that "all life is interrelated." He then elaborated further in a 1967 Christmas sermon, describing the implications of the peace Christ brings us:

> We are all caught in an inescapable network of mutuality, tied into a single garment of destiny. Whatever affects one directly, affects all indirectly. We are made to live together because of the interrelated structure of reality.[8]

Such observations are in line with the Catholic teaching of John Paul II. And Vatican II even expressly rejected discrimination on grounds that we are all created in the image of God.[9]

It is much more difficult to engage and embrace the idolatry of White supremacy when you know you're not God, but rather are made in God's image. Alas, the Church should be operating with these suppositions front and center. But

---

7. See Gustavo Gutiérrez, in Rosino Gibellini, ed., *Frontiers of Theology in Latin America* (Maryknoll, NY: Orbis, 1979), pp. 1–4; James Cone, "The gospel and the liberation of the poor," *The Christian Century* (Feb. 18, 1981), p. 166.

8. Martin Luther King, Jr., "A Christmas Sermon on Peace" (1967), in James M. Washington, ed., *A Testament of Hope: The Essential Writings and Speeches of Martin Luther King, Jr.* (San Francisco: Harper & Row, 1986), p. 254.

9. Vatican II, *Declaration on the Relation of the Church to Non-Christian Religions* (1965), p. 5.

its history right up to the present all too often is the story of the rich and powerful using Christian teachings to exploit Black people.

This awareness of human interconnection and religious history also supports the findings of Critical Race Theory and our contention that we are all participants in racism. On these grounds, if we are all residing in a racist society, that will impact our behavior and attitudes—rendering us racists or oppressed. Two modern American Catholic scholars, Vincent Rougeau and Gloria Purvis, agree that such insights are in line with Christian social teachings, dating back to Augustine of Hippo and his claim that sin/concupiscence impacts all we do.[10]

In compatibility with Christian understanding, all the scientific research suggests that racism is not in our best interests as human beings. It's not just bad for Black people; it's also not in the interests of whites. According to some civil rights activists and even evolutionary theories, we're all at our best when we are cooperating. Healthy *Homo sapiens* usually do what is in their best interests. We can only conclude that it's good for all of us to fight racism. It's not only "a Black thing." As John Paul II has noted, getting away from selfishness means returning to our true morally responsible selves. And the recent book by economist Heather McGhee makes the case for Black-White cooperation in the economy, arguing for the economic advantages of such cooperation.[11]

---

10. Augustine, *Confessions* (480), III.I.1; VI.XII.22; VI.XVI.26; Gloria Purvis, "Yes, Critical race theory is compatible with Catholicism. Here's why," *America* (July 6, 2021).

11. John Paul II, *Redemptor Hominis* (1979), pp. 32–34; McGhee.

Doing the Work: Why Cooperation Doesn't Come Easy

Since cooperation makes so much sense, why do we fight it? Why is racism "a thing" at all?

Biologist Robert Sapolsky provides helpful insights from a scientific perspective that even major religions, such as Christianity, Judaism, and Islam, can embrace. His observations conclude that it is inevitable that human beings, as the cooperative species we are, will form small groups which in turn lead to us/them mentalities.[12] We have already noted how the amygdala activates a sense of fear when we encounter those of another group—not just racial others, but also those of different sexes, geographic regions, or even those not of our family. Even oxytocin, which bonds us with our loved ones, is also biased. It causes us to feel aggressive toward those outside our immediate group. There's a lot in the brain that is rigged against cooperation.

Some Christians, Jews, and Muslims see these dynamics as manifestations of sin. These religions suggest that we absolutize preferences for our own immediate group or agendas by conferring divine status on the group, hence practicing idolatry. This is, at its core, one of the fundamental elements of racism—creating an absolute divinity of the racial experience. This divinity both fails to include those who are "other" and simultaneously rejects the absoluteness of God.

Yet the brain is plastic. It can change and be changed by repetitive behaviors with additional and strengthened new neural connections, leading to improved behavior. With relative scientific certainty, we can conclude that when the prefrontal cortex supervises the brain's functions, immediate

---

12.   Sapolsky, *Behave*, p. 388ff.

feelings of threat can be overridden; the worst impulses and prejudices can be overridden.[13]

So, we can do something about our instinctual racial biases. But how to implement this insight in us and in everyday life is the real challenge. Once again, biology offers some hints. Sapolsky offers an important observation in this regard: simply activating the frontal cortex of our brains does not abolish racism. In fact, such activation could reflect racial prejudice and merely indicate an effort to hide our prejudice or indicate that we feel badly about it. What is required to combat racism is to have tasks or strategies for this frontal cortex to undertake, which can overcome racism and habituate such tasks and attitudes.[14]

Breaking Down Barriers

Sapolsky sketches some strategies for people on both sides of the racial divide for enhancing a sense of cooperation, a feeling that we're all in this together. Though we do not think that it will ultimately be very helpful in ending racism, one strategy he suggests is to concentrate on positive images of the members of other races. Another strategy he proposes, about which we as authors disagree, is to try to identify with the members of the other race. Empathy is a function for activating the frontal cortex of the brain. Whites can help in the struggle against racism by imagining how they would feel were they on the short end of the statistics we have examined,

---

13. Susan T. Fiske, "Are We Born Racist?," Jason Marsh et al., eds., *Are We Born Racist: New Insights from Neuroscience and Positive Psychology* (Boston: Beacon, 2010), pp. 7–15.

14. Sapolsky, p. 417ff.

or the experiences Woodall has described. And Black people might try to imagine the social pressures and ostracism a White person might feel in some locales when he or she chides racist behaviors or policies by those in his or her social or professional network.

Though Woodall acknowledges the value in these suggestions, he raises a dissent primarily to the advice for Black people to have empathy for White people in their racism. It is racist even to consider asking Blacks for empathy for individuals who are responsible for police brutality, employment discrimination, or even gentrifying their neighborhood to make space for more whites. There may still be much value, however, in Black and White people both understanding the dynamics of racism.

Even better than empathy is contact, talking about racism with members of the other race and learning from them. Failing that, individuation is a good strategy: to think of members of another race not as a group but as individuals. As Mother Teresa once stated: "If I look at the mass, I will never act. If I look at one, I will." She says that if we just think about loving humanity or people in general, and not the individual person or specific situation, we are not likely to do anything about it.

It's easier to do what she says for Christians who, like Martin Luther and the Roman Catholic Focolare Movement, are used to seeing Christ in the individual who encounters us.[15]

---

15. Thomas Masters and Amy Uelmen, *Focolare: Living a Spirituality of Unity in the United States* (Hyde Park, NY: New City Press, 2011), p. 51; Martin Luther, *The Freedom of a Christian* (1520), in *Luther's Works*, Vol. 31 (St. Louis-Philadelphia: Concordia-Fortress, 1957), p. 351.

Evolutionary biologist David S. Wilson provides other insights drawn from the theory of evolution about what we can do to fight racism. Evolution teaches us that change does not happen through individuals, but via a species, in groups.[16] The basic advice is that we need first to become mindful of our values and goals, but then we should become a member of several worthwhile groups. Being part of a community is necessary because you can't cooperate alone, and if you don't know why you want to be part of a group you won't be of much use to the groups or to yourself. You can't fight racism alone—or at least it won't matter much in human history, and it won't make you happy.

There are plenty of extinct species in the history of the cosmos, so simply joining a group does not necessarily contribute helpfully to the evolutionary process. Successful groups need to be designed in such a way that they can meet new challenges, evolve without losing their purpose. This is best accomplished, Wilson contends, when the group is always on the lookout for best practices and learns from these successes. Evolutionary theory applied to these groups and to life is not so much discovering solutions that have never been tried but trying to identify why best practices work and how they can be spread across all domains of knowledge and possible applications. Evolution works that way, taking a best practice/organic development and spreading it out over all domains of life. A best-practice approach entails flexibility, a willingness to revise and change. Ideals never ultimately succeed in an evolving reality, because even "what is" changes. Realism always gets more done than idealism.

---

16.   Wilson, p. 217ff.

This commitment to spreading best practices over all domains leads to another characteristic of the groups anti-racist warriors will want to join. The most effective groups should aim to function not as lone rangers, but as healthy cells in multicellular societies. The group in your neighborhood or town dedicated to equality will only be of lasting value if it's part of a larger movement aimed at attacking racism everywhere. This feature accounts in part for the success of the Civil Rights Movement in the 1960s: small organizations and various national civil rights organizations that were all part of a national movement.

Biology does indeed teach us some lessons and give us some principles for enhancing cooperation in the struggle against racism. We'll try to envision more concretely how that might happen in the last chapter. But there is one more resource evolutionary science brings to the struggle against racism which might be worth considering. It's all about the evolution of religion and how the core of religion can help us enhance cooperation.

Evolution, Religion, and Cooperation

A new discipline in the field of religious studies has developed in recent decades—evolution of religion. Scholars use the insights of the theory of evolution to understand the origins of religion and why religion has continued to survive. The findings in this field have been very much in line with what evolution teaches us about *Homo sapiens*.

Anthropologists and biologists have observed that religion may have given *Homo sapiens* an advantage in cooperation. The gods *Homo sapiens* served were omniscient and could punish selfishness and misdeeds. Religion spiritualizes cooperative behavior. It provides a supernatural incentive for practicing behavior which restricts selfishness.[17] It also cultivates trust among adherents, which is essential for cooperation. Even patterned worship, when it takes the form of dancing or bodily movements of standing, sitting, and kneeling, can provide a sense of group cohesion among the faithful.[18]

George Kelsey, an often-overlooked teacher of Martin Luther King, Jr., and an inspiration for our insights about understanding racism as idolatry, noted that in early tribal religions there was a tendency to think of the members of the religion as elect or special people.[19] This parochial tendency tends to be overridden the more a religion like Christianity, Judaism, or Islam evolves into a world religion. However, in the case of Christianity, Kelsey notes, these ethnocentric tendencies are from time to time exploited by political and economic interests to distort the universal thrust of the faith. The resulting ethnocentric racism growing out of religion, contrary to the true character of religion, becomes a counter-religion, an idolatry.[20] Such racism is an idolatry because its adherents no longer place their faith in God, but in their own racial identity as the source of personal value. Racists practice naturalism, Kelsey contends. Racists seem to believe that the fundamental thing about human identity is the body we have.[21]

---

17. Matt Rossano, *Supernatural Selection: How Religion Evolved*, pp. 174–177; Nicholas Wade, *The Faith Instinct* (New York: Penguin Press, 2009), pp. 55–56.

18. Wade, *The Faith Instinct*, pp. 79–81,198ff.

19. George Kelsey, *Racism and the Christian Understanding of Man* (New York: Charles Scribner's Sons, 1965), p. 20.

20. Kelsey, pp. 9–10, 21–23, 26ff.

21. Kelsey, pp. 26–28.

Before World War II, Dietrich Bonhoeffer had identified idolatry as the core of modern sin. He observed that we have made ourselves our own creator and master, so that everything begins with ourselves and with obtaining the things of the world.[22]

Despite the potential for these distortions, the contribution universal religion can make to human collaboration and to combating racism is also made evident insofar as the parts of the brain associated with spiritual experience are the frontal neurons of the prefrontal cortex.[23] In other words, the very parts of the brain now stimulated by spiritual experiences are perhaps brain functions which first developed when human beings started engaging in spiritual experiences and are what make *Homo sapiens* distinct and uniquely capable of cooperation. Besides the activation of the frontal cortex, it seems that spirituality also stimulates the brain's anterior cingulate cortex. This cortex is the part of the brain situated between the frontal lobe and the limbic system, which contains our emotional circuits. The anterior cingulate cortex mediates these feelings and thoughts. It is crucial for social awareness and empathy.

Religious experience, then, enhances empathy and social awareness.[24] Again, this contributes to our cooperative abilities. It seems plausible to conclude, then, that religion has contributed to human evolution, helped make us the creatures we are. With its ability to nurture cooperation, it appears that religious faith has at least the potential to help us deal with racism (despite its institutional history of fostering racism, which

---

22. Bonhoeffer, p. 130.
23. Wade, p. 22; Newberg and Waldman, p. 42ff.
24. Newberg and Waldman, pp. 52–53.

must also be reckoned with). Spend more time in prayer, meditation, or Bible study. It's likely to make you more empathetic and likable, more human, and less prone to submit both to the anxieties of encounter with those of another race, and to the perks of White privilege.

Another way in which religion enhances morality and cooperation with "the other" relates to the brain chemicals secreted in spiritual exercises. Our use of the prefrontal cortex is rewarded, and its repeated use encouraged, by the secretion of "good feeling" brain chemicals, dopamine and oxytocin.[25]

As we've noted, these chemicals also enhance or are associated with bonding and therefore with sociality. We should examine how useful these chemicals are in the struggle with racism. Dopamine makes you more inclined to be sociable and perhaps less violent. Oxytocin can still bias you to be kinder to those of your own kin, so we cannot rely solely on its influence. We see, however, how a religious faith might support our efforts to be more fully human and to combat racism. Religion could help us move beyond it and lead us to empathize with and love each other.

When it saturates the brain, dopamine provides the inclination and the energy to reach out to the other. And the experience of oxytocin will enhance a sense of comfort and kindliness to those of the same faith; for example, it can make the White Christian feel more at ease with and nurturing of Black Christians and vice versa. It will not happen with religious nurture alone. Yet with the right kind of teaching in our

---

25. Newberg and Waldman, pp. 55–56; Patty Van Cappellen et al., "Effects of oxytocin administration on spirituality and emotional responses to meditation," *Social Cognitive and Affective Neuroscience* (Oct. 11, 2016): pp. 1579–1587.

religious communities, faith can contribute to breaking down the us-vs.-them barriers.

We have already noted that Vatican Council II, a meeting of the world's Catholic bishops in the 1960s, appealed to our all being created in the image of God, an affirmation which breaks down the significance of all human barriers between people. George Kelsey also appealed to this concept as a tool for undercutting the idolatry of racism. He contended that the concept of the image of God means that national differences do not determine who we are as human beings.[26] God, not race, determines who we are, and so the idol of race is shattered!

We've already pointed out how perhaps Ibram X. Kendi is right, that the way to end racism is to abolish all references to race (see his book *How to Be an Antiracist*). We would add that the destruction of race as a thing is critical if we are to truly move beyond the vestiges of our violent history. It is true that simply removing the nomenclature from our vocabulary only leaves space for more categories to form, as this is what humans do: we organize and group ourselves together. The challenge, though, is that the social constructions of race are not simply about identity and who belongs with whom; race also organizes our entire society in ways that determine access to resources, political reality, and socioeconomic outcome.

Another way to break down the us vs. them barrier is to help Christians see unity in the radical love of Jesus, the blood and marital union we all share with him. When one believes that we are all married to Jesus, that we are all kin to one another, both theology and science show that the

---

26. Kelsey, pp. 29–30.

amygdala and the fear it nurtures can be de-activated, leading us to behave more humanly toward members of other communities.[27] Martin Luther King, Jr., made a similar point in clarifying that Jesus Christ is about blending opposites (see *The Strength to Love*).

When religious people react with fear and judgment to believers of other religions, they need to remember their amygdala-inspired fear of "the other" is likely skewing their reactions and gut-level perceptions of those believers. Like all of us, religious people need to exercise emotional intelligence, to have the prefrontal cortex kick in when relating to those of another faith. And as we've shown in this chapter, prayer and other spiritual exercises can make that happen.

Evolution also helps us recognize how to deal with racism. These dynamics are related to the dynamics of the human brain: The eventual repression of racism—or rather, of noticing and/or fearing ethnic differences (the root of racism)—is natural, as human beings are geared toward higher and higher levels of cooperation. Indeed, Christianity recognizes that we all share a common sense of what is good—the natural law (Romans 2:14–15, for example).[28]

Evolution demonstrates how, at our best, human beings reject racism. It also provides some tools or ways of thinking

27.   For the religious background, see John M. Perkins, *One Blood: Parting Words to the Church on Earth* (Chicago: Moody Press, 2018); Chiara Lubich "I have only one Spouse on Earth," available at *focolare.org/en/news/2016/09/25/chiara-lubich-ho-un-solo-sposo-sulla-terra/*; Martin Luther, *The Freedom of a Christian*, in *Luther's Works*, Vol. 31, p. 351. For the scientific side, see Newberg and Waldman, especially pp. 43, 137ff.; Wheeler and Fiske.

28.   See also *Catechism of the Catholic Church*, 1905ff; Martin Luther King, Jr., "Letter from a Birmingham Jail" (1963).

to orient us in that struggle. And evolution even suggests that religion also has a significant contribution to make in challenging racism.

What Evolution Can Teach Us about Our Institutional Best Practices

In this chapter we've been trying to summarize the lessons taught by evolution and religion for individuals in the struggle against racism. But evolution, and to a lesser extent religion, also have some lessons about best practices for institutions, which also need to be addressed in the struggle against racism, as we saw in chapter one. An examination of *Homo sapiens'* evolution reveals that human beings need communities to thrive. For Woodall and Ellingsen it's been the Church and our local communities in the South. Consider your own communities. What are the best-functioning communities you are a part of, and the best institutional practices they employ?

Economist Elinor Ostrom, who received the Nobel Prize in 2009, outlined eight core design principles for institutional design. Ostrom's principles, many of which may date back to the earliest hunter-gatherer institutions of *Homo sapiens,* would not tolerate racial or other forms of injustice. We would do well to assess the institutions of modern American society in their light. The principles are:

1. Strong group identity and understanding of purpose. What group or society has a chance to thrive if it does not know what it is doing?

2. Proportional equivalence between benefits and costs. This rules against inequality in workloads. Leaders should only get more if they do more. Consider what this principle might entail for the American economy.

3. Fair and inclusive decision-making. Consensus is a wise method. Top-down regulations do not work well in most groups; then the group's activities do not belong to everyone, but just to those with power. Considering the domination of whiteness in the American system, implementing this principle in our institutions could have important implications in the struggle against racism.

4. Monitoring agreed-upon behaviors. We always lapse in our good intentions. It is good to call ourselves to accountability. A group or society with no standards always languishes. Have we become too content with the lower standards and the call "to be good to yourself" which so predominates in American society today?

5. Graduated sanction. When members of the group are not executing their responsibilities, friendly reminders are the best place to start. But when they fail, some form of punishment or exclusion needs to be exercised. And if these subsequent chastisements are not carried out, the standards of the organization inevitably decline. Corporate executives and billionaires, and in many ways White people in general, often face less severe penalties when they "fail," if they are held accountable at all—while other people who are not White or wealthy experience more severe punishments (and often for lesser infractions).

6. Fast, fair conflict resolution. Most modern American institutions are a lot better at dodging conflict or postponing resolution—particularly when it would mean admitting wrongdoing.

7. Local autonomy. If the group is part of a larger society, local groups need to be given maximum freedom. This and the next principle have implications for the establishment of Black interest groups and the contribution they might make to the broader society.

8. Polycentric governance. Smaller groups are often part of larger societies. The dynamics between the small groups and the larger body should mirror the way individuals relate to the broader organization, as articulated in the first six principles.[29]

David Sloan Wilson, an evolutionary biologist, notes that these principles well express how all institutions and societies, like species, must evolve. Churches need to learn these lessons too. These principles, he contends, have been reflected in evolutionary history in species that have survived and thrived. If we want our businesses and institutions to thrive, they need to embody these principles. And the fact that most institutions and societies have not reflected the principles fully explains why most do not survive. When we analyze our racist structures and institutions by means of these insights, we'll see that and why they're not thriving.

Only when racism is curtailed can our institutions embody these principles. But maybe by implementing them our institutions can begin to evolve to something more just. We'll try to envision how to implement this project in the next chapter. When we do that, though, we don't want to forget the other lessons taught by evolution. We learn from it, above all, that the name of the game is cooperation. The principles of Ostrom are just ways of incarnating cooperation.

Evolutionary biology also teaches us that the way to thrive is not with ideology but by making sense of best practices. Which practices will best facilitate human cooperation, along with our cooperation with the waves of life and other patterns of our cosmos, and the other living things sharing our living space?

---

29.   Wilson, p. 116ff.

Belonging to a religion does not ensure avoidance of racism, and secularists can certainly be anti-racist. For as human beings, atheists are as biologically inclined to cooperation as any other. But it sure does not hurt to have faith, an activity which over a lifetime solidifies the brain connections which keep the front part of your brain active, to build strong neural connections between it and the rest of the brain.

Armed by all these spiritual and physical assets, let's see where faith and biology might take us in our challenge to racial idolatry—if we don't let all the mistakes our political and religious institutions have made over the centuries get in the way.

Chapter 5

Destroying White Supremacy: The Beloved Community ... How Do We Get There?

In some respects, this is the most important chapter of the book. We have already noted that our entire existence as human beings, from the educational system, our jobs and professional fields, and the media and entertainment which we consume, to our places of worship and the communities in which we live, is impacted in one way or another by this phenomenon called racism. In this chapter, we focus on what we can do to change that.

We stress that racism impacts the broader institutions of society, including White people and their participation in these institutions. The truth is that discussions of racism have been minimized to reflect only individualized aggressions. Racism in all its manifestations is a byproduct of psychological reactions that respond to stimulated brain activity due to unfamiliarity with others and/or anxiety. Regulating and controlling these reactions, however, will not solve racism nor destroy the religious idolatry that is White supremacy. So, we must push further in our quest to eradicate it—as we do in this chapter.

As we have defined in this book, racism is a condition in which human beings deny other human beings their divine right to power, love, and a sound mind, based primarily on the false premise of racial categories—Black and white. The very presence of these two oppressive (and bogus) categories creates a kind of spell on our minds that places us into a "trance" of race, leaving us blinded to the true reality of the human condition.

The first way we defeat the idolatry that is racism is by making space for the voices and stories of people who are most impacted by and closest to oppression. We've already noted how the findings of evolutionary theory and the nature of religious experience emphasize the virtues of human cooperation, which requires that all voices (most especially "the voiceless," the marginalized) be heard. But reducing this effort simply to organizing "community conversations" and pushing diversity and inclusion initiatives without centering the lives, voices, and experiences of those most impacted by and marginalized from these racist realities—in short, Black people—is at best performative and at worst violently traumatizing.

Highlighting the voices and experiences of Black people is still the bare minimum and does not call into question the power dynamics of racist violence that continue to challenge our ability to cooperate with one another. History has shown how the inherent vulnerability of human beings allows racism to creep into the "unawares" of Black *and* White spaces. It even impacts our ability to fight against these inhumane conditions. Liberation theologian Paulo Freire was right: because of our sinful human nature, almost always, during the initial stage of the struggle, the oppressed, instead of striving for liberation, tend themselves to become oppressors, or "sub-oppressors." The very structure of their thought has been conditioned by the contradictions of the concrete, existential situation by which they were shaped. Their ideal is to be men; but for them, to be men is to be oppressors. This is their model of humanity.[1]

---

1. Paulo Freire, *Pedagogy of the Oppressed, 30th Anniversary Edition*, trans. Myra Ramos (New York and London: Bloomsbury, 1998), p. 45.

In order that we not let our all-too-flawed suggestions get in the way of true cooperation, we hasten to add first that we see ourselves as merely offering some potential best practices. We are trying to offer suggestions which reflect a consensus in regard to where organizations and leaders of the movement for Black lives and human rights meet our daily lived experiences. If you know better practices or have seen ones we have omitted, we welcome you to be in dialogue with us. Above all, though, let's keep in mind what we have in common: We want to end racism. Let's be united in the commitment to enhancing human cooperation; we are confident that it's the key to human survival and thriving and that it's best to do it through advocacy groups and community organizations.

This commitment to cooperation or building alliances for the sake of action shows up in all sorts of recent literature on race, including books by Don Lemon (*This is the Fire*, particularly chapter seven), Heather McGhee (*The Sum of Us*), and Ibram X. Kendi (*How to Be an Antiracist*). Dr. King advocated for this sort of interracial collaboration, and it was earlier practiced by Adam Clayton Powell, Sr., of the Abyssinian Baptist Church in New York.[2] We're trying to walk in the footsteps of these Black preaching giants by outlining some concrete ways they made such cooperation happen.

Crucial to this shared commitment is the realization that we all play a role in the proliferation of racism. We conclude that active amygdalae predispose us toward racial biases; whites need to add to this information an admission that they benefit from the present system as a result of these biases. Only if we agree to the reality that, as individuals, we're all on edge

---

2. *A Testament of Hope: The Essential Writings of Martin Luther King, Jr.*, ed. James Washington (San Francisco: Harper & Row, 1986), p. 264; King, "Remaining Awake Through a Great Revolution," in *A Testament of Hope*," p. 270ff.

with each other, and that whites have become the standard for humanity while everyone else was made the oppressed "other," can we be sure to have a common agenda and enemy. Remember that these biases can be controlled by monitoring your frontal cortex and keeping control of your emotions.

Studying the data in the first chapter shows how whites have created and enjoyed racial advantages. To negate the damage from these advantages, we need to lift and embrace the stories of Black people, who have been negatively impacted. We are proceeding with the areas of racism in America which we noted in the first chapter. Almost everything on that list was drawn from the aims or purpose statements of leading civil rights organizations in the United States, but we are happy to add more issues to the list that we might have missed. One of the controversial agendas we are presenting as a best practice is reparations—but we've got a spin on this that might be a useful compromise. Let's start with how to end racist practices in policing.

Justice in Policing

How do we end the police shootings of Black men, women, and children; get fairer criminal sentencing; and do something about the disproportionate Black population in prison? White cops are prone to be more anxious, to have their amygdala in overdrive when encountering Black men. And with all the negative Black stereotypes we've discussed but not yet stamped out, Black cops have amygdala overdrive in the presence of other Black people as well.

What can we do about this? One remedy—which according to Louis Dekmar, former president of the International Association of Chiefs of Police, is becoming more accepted among police departments—is to de-emphasize the role of officer discretion in policing in favor of adherence to departmental policies regarding the purpose of patrols: when to arrest, what happens when you stop someone, and when to use force. Among the departmental policies which might be implemented is an emphasis on community partnerships, so that when police encounter suspicious or dangerous behavior, they are trained to refer the party in question to the agency which can best help the individual with shelter, food, education, or other resources.[3]

Another policy, Dekmar suggests, might be to confront prevailing American police practices regarding the use of firearms, as most are trained to shoot assailants in the chest. By contrast, European officers are trained to shoot to disable the assailant, to aim for arms and legs. Notably, the murder of George Floyd in Minneapolis has finally convinced most departments that knee- and chokeholds are inhumane and must be prohibited as a law enforcement practice. In response, some police departments are exploring training in non-lethal Asian martial arts techniques for restraining suspects. None of this will work on the streets of America without adequate training of officers, including sensitizing police to their inherent biases and training them to see themselves and the suspect as part of the whole to which they belong, to remember the basic lessons of *Homo sapiens*' cooperative orientation. It is important at this point to recognize that this problem is not just about the police and is not going to be solved merely by defunding them, even if that would mean reallocating funding given to police to other government agencies.

These are all fine in theory, but it is going to take changes in policy to end behaviors and policies by law enforcement

---

3.   Louis Dekmar, private interview, April 2, 2021.

which seem to foster systemic racism. In chapter two, we outlined the prevailing policy of law enforcement, "predictive (or statistical) policing." We noted how identifying suspects based on what "kinds" of people commit most of the crimes in a municipality leads cops not just into a siege mentality but is also likely to bias them more against African Americans and increasingly Hispanics, who statistically are arrested for crimes in disproportionate numbers to the size of their populations.

This mindset not only exacerbates the sense of panic the brains of police may already have toward Black men. In Black neighborhoods it creates an ethos in which every resident could be a suspect. This establishes an adversarial relationship between police and those whom they serve. The amygdala works for Black residents and new immigrants when encountering White police, and the adversarial relationships between the cops and the community make things worse.

As far as police officers and departments go, this mode is not going to be readily abandoned. It seems to make sense to have cops in neighborhoods which are statistically most likely to require police intervention and protection.[4] Alternatives have been developed, but not widely implemented. One special strategy has been termed Community Policing. Essentially this policing model proceeds with the assumption that police rarely can solve public safety problems alone, and it encourages the kind of interactive partnerships with relevant stakeholders already noted. The range of potential partners is large, and these partnerships can be used to accomplish the two interrelated goals of developing solutions to problems through collaborative problem solving and improving public trust. The public should play a role in prioritizing and

---

4.   Dekmar, private interview, April 2, 2021.

addressing public safety problems. In short, those who police the community should know the community. Police are there as members of the community in cooperation with other partners, not just there to defend or contain the community, as in the prevailing model.

The best practices suggested already regarding implementing partnerships between police and helping agencies in the community, with cops seeing it as part of their job to refer people they encounter to these agencies, are in line with the community policing model. Obviously, a premium is placed on cooperation with this model, and it also gains insights from the evolution-based findings of Robert Sapolsky, that we progress further in cooperation when we have contact with members of other races (see chapter four). The Community Policing model entails that law enforcement know the community and the community knows them. That puts a damper on the amygdala and the fear its activation produces.

Further observations from Nobel Prize–winning economist Elinor Ostrom, from whom we learned how organizations can function optimally, can help us here. In the 1970s she conducted a study of small police force performance in comparison to city-wide police forces and found that small police forces locally controlled are more effective than a city-wide force in meeting citizen demands. Apparently, this is a function of police knowing the community better, and the community and helping agencies having more say in how crime is addressed.[5]

Another promising program, which was instituted by the National Urban League in New York, is social media

---

5.   Elinor Ostrom and Gordon Whitaker, "Does Local Community Control of Police make a Difference? Some Preliminary Findings," *American Journal of Political Science* 17(1) (Feb. 1973): pp. 48–76.

conversations between citizens and police officers, along with changes in how police respond to 911 calls. Citizens can request service, and police determine if a crime is in progress. If it is determined that no crime is transpiring, police offer alternative options for assistance. Nationalizing this program to help reduce tensions between police and African Americans is worth serious consideration.

These programs accord with Ostrom's biologically friendly eight principles for institutions, for community policing fosters a stronger group identity. Benefits and costs are more equivalent (for what might be lost in efficiency, as police are not so quick to act on "likelihood," thereby perhaps temporarily leading to higher rates of crime, is balanced by more trust and less abuse of power). In addition, the whole system is likely to be fairer, especially if effective monitoring is part of the package. There is clearly a lot more autonomy, and if all the community entities are truly cooperating (and if, for example, the helping agencies can even be in dialogue with local gangs), you have a successful venture and evolutionary process.

Is this a best practice that could/should serve as a nationwide model for eradicating racism in police work? If not, let's be in dialogue about better options. It is of interest to note that something like this model was advocated as long ago as 1968 by Martin Luther King, Jr., as he wrote in the essay "A Testament of Hope":

Obviously, something desperately needs to be done to correct this. . . . Our police forces simply must develop an attitude of courtesy and respect for the ordinary citizen. . . . In the larger sense, police must cease being occupation troops in the ghetto and start protecting its residents. Yet very few cities have really faced up to this problem and tried to do some-thing about it.[6]

Again, these are great ideas. Several of them have already been implemented in some communities. But the implemen-tation has been done locally, only under certain police chiefs, and so many of these reforms have not been made permanent. We need to see these ideas become expectations in the guilds of law enforcement, and a first step might be to mandate that all local police departments be accredited with the assurance that the practices discussed are now part of the accreditation standards of the Commission on Accreditation for Law En-forcement Agencies.

Racial Justice in the Courts and the Prison Population

Data have already been presented to indicate the racial dispar-ity in prosecution of crimes, sentencing, and even false convic-tions. Highly publicized verdicts of "not guilty" in high-profile cases taken up in recent years by the Innocence Project further underline the fallibility and racial bias of the criminal legal sys-tem. Why is it still happening? We have already indicated the brain dynamics which are no doubt a root cause. The typically White prosecutor or judge is neurologically disposed to see the Black suspect or defendant as a threat to the community. The brain's amygdala is sending that warning and as we have seen, Black prosecutors are also likely to relate that way to Black de-fendants because of media portrayals of Blackness. The frontal cortex can control the amygdalae of our brains, but this be-havior needs reinforcements to establish strong enough brain connections to make this control habitual.

---

6.   King, "A Testament of Hope," in *A Testament of Hope*, p. 325.

Placing quotas on convictions and prosecutions might not be fruitful, but if prosecutors and judges continue to use criminal convictions to evaluate job performance, and the media continue to make the public aware of the imbalance in prosecution and sentencing, it could be a useful check and balance. The media need to be held equally accountable for the imbalanced coverage of Black crime on whites. Studies by the Sentencing Project have noted that although most US homicides are intra-racial, media accounts over-represent Black-on-White crime.[7] Let's keep amplifying these disparities, as well as pressuring lawmakers to ensure that disparities in public policy do not further contribute to these imbalances.

As for the imbalance in the prison population, we have already noted that African Americans make up one-third of the present US prison population (while making up less than 13% of the total US population). The increase in numbers is also related to the marked growth of the prison population, having increased 500% in the last forty years, but of course this is not the whole story.[8] One factor in this increase is the institution of more mandatory sentencing legislation beginning in the years of the Ronald Reagan presidency (especially 1987). Some of these guidelines unwittingly—or wittingly—discriminate against Blacks, notably the difference in sentencing structures for powder cocaine and crack cocaine charges. Blacks are more typically prosecuted for crack cocaine offenses, which have been assigned more severe mandatory sentences than the use of powder.

7. Nazgol Ghandnoosh, "Race and Punishment: Racial Perceptions of Crime and Support for Punitive Policies" (2014).
8. Lewis.

Other practices that need to be abolished include mandatory life sentences without parole for children, solitary confinement, and capital punishment, for Blacks typically bear the brunt of these actions. Of those serving life without parole, more than 48% are Black. More whites are executed than Blacks, but since 41% of those executed are Blacks, that percentage far exceeds the percentage of all Americans who are Black. Likewise, though only 33% of those who are in prison are Black, a higher percentage (as high as 62% in some facilities) of those in solitary confinement are Black.[9]

Another issue which some think contributes to the marked rise of the prison population is governments' contracting the prison system to private corporations. Profits have been pronounced for these companies (like Corrections Corporation of America), while local governments saved money.[10] It is in the interests of the bottom line of these companies to have more prisoners in the pipeline. Black men offer a good supply.

It may be wise to use the language of the prison abolition movement and just end prisons once and for all, using healthy alternatives to correctional control and supervision, such as inpatient treatment, work release, and even restitution, opportunities that data proves can be effective in rehabilitation, re-entry and ultimately redemption. It is realistic, however, to

---

9. See Prison Policy Initiative's page on race and ethnicity (https://www.prisonpolicy.org/research/race_and_ethnicity); Bureau of Justice Statistics, "Capital Punishment, 2020 - Statistical Tables" (https://bjs.ojp.gov/library/publications/capital-punishment-2020-statistical-tables); Ryan T. Sakoda and Jessica T. Simes, "Solitary Confinement and the U.S. Prison Boom," *Criminal Justice Policy Review* 32(1) (2019): pp. 66–102.

10. Matt Taibbi, *The Divide: American Injustice in the Age of the Wealth Gap* (New York: Spiegel & Grau, 2014), especially pp. 214–216.

acknowledge that some form of correctional control will need to exist for the foreseeable future. Some prison abolitionists suggest that 10% of the current prison system will remain necessary to maintain, yet the overall goal of divestment of correctional control remains possible. Of course, lower poverty rates tend to mean lower crime rates too. Let's examine now some best practices for ending racism in our economy.

Ending Economic Racism

We have previously examined the dismal statistics showing racial discrimination against African Americans in starting companies, getting jobs, and getting promotions. As we have noted, we must make an appeal to our "better angels," the uniquely human part of our brains, to keep our fears in check in the interests of equity and of heightening the cooperation which makes us truly human. This is certainly in line with Catholic thinking, which has always contended that economics must serve human interests, not the other way around. Martin Luther took a similar position regarding human institutions.[11]

The more we get out these statistics and let them be known, the more business pressures (losing potential customers through boycotts because of evidence of practicing racism) may influence people to just do the right thing (the "invisible hand" of Adam Smith). Government enforcement of anti-discrimination practices and laws in making loans is also a relevant tool. Affirmative action policies and quotas have a continuing role to play as well. Nor should we forget the ingenuity

---

11.   *Catechism of the Catholic Church*, 2426; Martin Luther, "The Gospel for Epiphany" (1521–1522), in *Luther's Works*, Vol. 52 (St. Louis-Philadelphia: Concordia-Fortress, 1974), p. 173.

of Black people who have been successful in various American industries, despite the realities of racism; we must find ways to uplift, amplify, and support them, too.

Perhaps these trends could be used in support of reparations, countering again White complaints that they owned no slaves, and that living Black people have not been victimized by slavery. We might grant this for the sake of argument, making the case that Black families since Reconstruction have been hurt by these practices, and so have not had the opportunity to build wealth like White families who were not so burdened by this career-killing prejudice. Reparation amounts could be based on cases where the discrimination could be shown to have transpired and calculated according to the date and salary involved with appropriate calculations for accumulated wealth in those years up to the present. Some of this reparation money might be invested back into building Black businesses today.

Another version of reparations has been offered by William Darity and A. Kirsten Mullen. They argue for reparations in terms of the promise of "forty acres and a mule" for freedmen voiced by Sherman and some Republicans after the Civil War (a promise never delivered). Darity and Mullen calculated that forty million acres should therefore have been allocated to the four million freedmen. The value of that land today would be between 1.5 to two trillion dollars. This means the 3.5 million or more African Americans who can trace their ancestors to American slaves would be entitled to $40 thousand to $60 thousand per person.[12]

---

12. William A. Darity Jr. and A. Kirsten Mullen, *From Here to Equality: Reparations for Black Americans in the Twenty-First Century* (Chapel Hill, NC: University of North Carolina Press, 2020), especially pp. 2, 4, 31.

Further research may reveal other areas in which discrimination could demand reparations and we welcome those findings for consideration as well. But let us not be naïve in this era of the globalized free market gone mad. We are living in an economy which is bad for everyone, except the top 1%. The middle class (White and Black) is getting squeezed. Although there has been an increase in household income in America since 1970 (with losses recently occasioned by the COVID pandemic), the growth has been tilted to upper-income households. Upper-income families have the greatest aggregate income, which is startling when you consider that we are talking about 5% of the population getting 48% of the income. It also means that the bottom 95% of Americans have not experienced any of the growth in half a century.

There are a lot of factors causing these developments. Trends like the excessive cost of political campaigns (which favor the rich), the tax cuts for the rich that these "purchased politicians" have passed, the internet revolution leading to the diminution of low-skilled jobs, the corresponding decline of labor unions, and the rise of a cultural narcissism which advocates for the goodness of greed and self-expression at the expense of community have all played significant roles in creating our present economic climate. Accounting for these economic and cultural developments and how to correct them deserves a book in itself.

Public works projects are certainly one promising option for resolving the ill effects of racism. Even Donald Trump recognized that we need to repair our crumbling infrastructure, and millions of good-paying government jobs could be created this way. Perhaps his Republican colleagues in the House and Senate might join with his successors to "make America great" in this way. Policies which help increase homeownership in the Black community (with more tax breaks for smaller houses, not just for larger ones) could also go a long way toward overcoming the racial wealth gap (by at least 30%), since home ownership is a major component in creating wealth.[13] But for our purposes, one possible way of immediately remedying the inequalities in our economy is a venerable one (though many call it radical): guaranteed income, or universal basic income. Though this approach received attention from Democratic presidential candidate Andrew Yang in 2020 and from Facebook founder Mark Zuckerberg (in his Harvard commencement speech in 2017), it is not at this time a viable option among the opinion- and policy-makers. Some political conservatives would even call it socialism.

The intriguing thing about this attitude and its permeation throughout American culture is that as recently as 1960, 70% of Americans claimed to believe that government should guarantee a job and minimum standard of living.[14] We need to tackle the problem of why this support has diminished. In part it's related to racial stereotypes, a feeling in White society that Black people get all the handouts.[15] It's certainly a reflection of our loss of the human spirit of cooperation and maybe of an increase in corporate investments in political and social conditioning.

The State of Alaska has had a universal basic income program in place since 1982. Richard Nixon advocated something like it during his term in office, as did famed

---

13. McGhee, p. 275ff.
14. American National Elections Studies, reported in McGhee, p. 28.
15. American National Elections Studies, reported in McGhee, p.33ff.

propagandist for the American Revolution Thomas Paine.[16] With such aims in mind Thomas Jefferson wrote to James Madison in 1785:

But the consequences of this enormous inequality producing so much misery to the bulk of mankind, legislators cannot invent too many devices for dividing property. . . . Whenever there is in any country uncultivated lands and unemployed poor, it is clear that the laws of property have been so far extended as to violate natural right. . . .. If, for the encouragement of industry we allow it [the land] to be appropriated, we must take care that other employment be furnished to those excluded from the appropriation.[17]

And Alexander Hamilton wrote in *The Federalist Papers*:

Happy it is when the interest which the government has in the preservation of its own power, coincides with a proper distribution of the public burdens, and tends to guard the least wealthy part of the community from oppression![18]

No less an important voice in the Black community than Martin Luther King, Jr., saw this economic model as a solution to America's ills. He insisted that the guaranteed income "must be pegged to the median income of society, not at the lowest levels."[19]

No doubt skeptics of this proposal will find it untenable, assuming it will encourage people not to work. Dr. King offers a sound rebuttal to such critiques. Work is something people

---

16. Thomas Paine, "Agrarian Justice" (1797).
17. Thomas Jefferson, "Thomas Jefferson to James Madison, 28 Oct. 1785," in *The Founders' Constitution*, Philip B. Kurland and Ralph Lerner, eds. (University of Chicago Press and Liberty Fund).
18. Alexander Hamilton, "No. 36," in *The Federalist Papers*, p. 240.
19. King, "Where Do We Go From Here: Chaos or Community?" (1967), in *A Testament of Hope*, p. 616.

want to do, he argued, for through it "the dignity of the individual will flourish" when "decisions concerning his life are in his own hands." And from a purely economic standpoint, it is good for all of America if the poor are able to earn enough to be consumers for the long haul.[20] Getting the poor out of poverty by ending discrimination in all its subtle (not just blatant) forms seems to be all about cooperation among *Homo sapiens*, about how, when we cooperate, the species is enhanced.

Along the same lines, the words of famed American Christian social ethicist Reinhold Niebuhr are a useful summary of what we need to do to overcome economic racism, regardless of which system we use. Racism could only be ended, he argued in 1968, by means of providing the necessary economic tools to the Black community so that it is no longer dependent on government help.[21] Would not even the Right welcome that outcome?

Ending Housing Discrimination

There are federal laws which seek to end redlining. The Community Reinvestment Act, for example, requires banks to make investments in low-income neighborhoods by making home loans more accessible to those residents and by having more branch locations in those communities. It will then be more likely that the small businesses in the community will get access to loans. Like most laws, the proof of effectiveness is in the details of implementation. Given its relative ineffectiveness in the forty years it has been on the books, the Community Reinvestment Act may need some federal enhancements by

---

20. King, "Where Do We Go From Here?" pp. 248, 252.
21. Niebuhr, p. 252.

attaching explicit affirmative action rubrics to the law. This is in line with the suggestions of Sheryll Cashin (in *White Space, Black Hood*) that the best way to end our residential resource segregation is by investing in poor Black communities.

Municipal zoning is also an area in need of increased monitoring. Local governments can and do, through zoning and ordinance decisions, prohibit disadvantaged communities from creating wealth by limiting what businesses can open in the community, while allowing business development in more privileged communities. Understanding public policy and local politics is therefore crucial in getting racism out of the housing market. Integration of mixed-income and mixed-ethnic communities might be effective if White flight out of such neighborhoods and gentrification of lower-income communities would ever stop. The challenge with using policy to address the systemic failures of the past is that it was policies that enabled present conditions in the first place—conditions that make economic mobility for one community possible while keeping others struggling even to maintain their foothold. Policies are only as strong as the priorities and authority of those who enforce them.

Now, housing could be a point for implementing reparations in the form of reconciliatory payments to descendants of slaves who were denied economic opportunities in the past. This is a solution many readers, even those consciously committed to justice, will likely find problematic. "Reparations," it is said in some White circles, "are unjust. My family never owned slaves. We were not even here! Why should we have to pay Black people who never were slaves themselves?" Well, let's follow that argument for a moment. Black families, even those who have "made it," have been denied access to generations of economic opportunity by redlining policies and discrimination in education, business, and other areas we have discussed. They may be now living in homes comparable to those of their White neighbors, but there is a measurable difference in how much wealth Black neighborhoods accumulate in value versus that of other communities. To add insult to injury, those who live in sub-standard or temporary housing today may be there because previous generations, who were denied equitable housing options, could not supply their children with financial assistance on the down payment for a nice house—or any house at all. Maybe the parents were offered lower pay than their White counterparts, who can now help their child afford that better home.

This vicious generational cycle and the gentrification of Black-legacy neighborhoods, where real estate and property taxes have skyrocketed, may account for why young Black families are more likely to rent today in general, and less likely to be able to buy a house in the inner city. Given the case we made for the generational effects of racist policies for Black families, do reparations make more sense or seem more just? If not, what is a better way we can all cooperate to end housing discrimination?

Environmental Justice

One of the greatest threats to our collective ability to build the beloved community is the existential threat that is environmental racism. The world around us is experiencing major changes in weather patterns, a climate crisis, worldwide infrastructure failures, and natural disasters of intensities we have never witnessed before. We have seen the disparate impact that these environmental challenges have had on humanity; the brunt of the force of nature reacting to human pollution is unequally and unfairly experienced in Black and other non-White communities. Once again, we need to get the frontal lobes of our brains in overdrive to make sure that our common destiny and cooperation are at the forefront of all we do to mitigate the real harms of environmental injustice.

There are several pillars which need our immediate attention if we are to be serious about resolving the ills of White supremacy in our environment. We derive the next set of policy proposals from the "Equitable and Just National Climate Platform," a coalition of leading US environmental justice and national environmental groups. The platform's goals are:

- Address the legacy of pollution: Ambitious climate solutions must acknowledge and address the legacy of pollution and other environmental harms in over-burdened communities.

- Make justice and equity a priority: Without these central aspects, the inequality of the carbon-based economy will be replicated as we build a clean and renewable energy economy.

- Reduce greenhouse gas pollution: Locally harmful air pollution disproportionately affects low-income areas and communities of color.

- Transition to a clean energy future: High-quality clean energy jobs, health protections, job-training programs, and fair and equitable working conditions must be extended to all communities, especially those with high underemployment and unemployment and those historically reliant on fossil fuel energy.

- Reduce transportation pollution: We must rebuild our transportation system so that it is fair, equitable, clean, and improves people's mobility as it cleans up the air.

- Rebuild infrastructure and housing: They must better withstand the harmful impacts of climate change in all communities.

- Demand a just national climate agenda: It must provide sustainable investment that will not impose an undue social and economic cost on overburdened and vulnerable communities.

- Be on a path to limit warming to 1.5 degrees Celsius: The United States must commit to ambitious emission reduction goals and contribute equitably to global efforts to stabilize the climate system by limiting global warming.

Efforts to deregulate environmental protections, often sponsored by special interest groups like the fossil fuel industry and other multinational corporations, have continued despite the serious urgency to correct the harm that has been caused by human wastefulness and commercial excess. Restoration of former federal policies like the Clean Air Act and the Clean Water Act would bring us closer to our goal of a more equitable environment that would be safe for all communities.

This requires, as in the case of fighting for racial equity in our courts, that we get the statistics out into the popular consciousness. A big step in this direction will be to get environmental organizations, such as the Sierra Club, Greenpeace, and Friends of Earth, to be heavily involved in public policy decisions that ultimately have significant implications for generations of Black communities.

The Green New Deal, the federal legislative proposal that is currently being pushed before and within the US Congress, may be moving in that direction, as one coauthor is Black social policy expert Rhiana Gunn-Wright. Ultimately the fate of our nation and world on climate issues will be determined by politics and economics. Instituting any of the projects outlined above will take the cooperation of Washington and Wall Street (along with Beijing, New Delhi, and most every major capital in the world) if we are going to ensure that "green" is not tinted White more than—or at the expense of—Black.

Ending Racism in Education

There are at least two distinct levels which must be addressed if we are to end racism in the educational system. Both racism in the curriculum and racism and classism in the delivery of that curriculum need serious attention. Let's start with what is perhaps the easier one: curriculum. The educational establishment and even corporate elites, academics, and public officials have begun consciously to acknowledge the ways in which White narratives have predominated in American history to the exclusion of Black narratives—except for those which record the subservient, impoverished aspects of Black history—and how White narratives legitimize the reason there is a subservient, impoverished narrative of Blacks in the first place.

The public's ignorance of Black contributions to this nation's history remains appalling. Most Americans would be surprised to learn, for example, that about 4% of George Washington's Revolutionary Army was Black. African

Americans comprised 10% of the Union's forces during the Civil War. We might know about G. W. Carver's invention of peanut butter, but few know that the traffic light is the invention of a Black man named Garrett Morgan or that Brother Lewis H. Latimer made a major contribution to the development of the light bulb, a feat most credit to Thomas Edison instead. There were even Black millionaires in the nineteenth century, such as Jeremiah Hamilton, Robert Gordon, and Mary Ellen Pleasant. As early as 1907 a Black college student, Alain LeRoy Locke, was awarded a Rhodes Scholarship. The man who made the automatic lubricating system for train and ship engines was an African American, Elijah McCoy. Another brother, Frederick M. Jones, invented refrigerated trucks. These are just a few details of Black history that are often neglected in the discourse of history, but this neglect can be resolved.

However, a more accurate and inclusive teaching of American history alone will not in itself solve the problem of alleged under-achievement in our schools. We say "alleged" because the very standard of achievement in this context may reflect racist renderings of knowledge and includes standards that do not acknowledge the material condition of the lives of students. Ellingsen has an African American colleague at the Interdenominational Theological Center who chides his students that doing the assigned work is not just a matter of reading dead White men, for they (the students) are not attending enough to the books by living Black authors. We can attest to the way that, when a teacher presents Black people in history whose contributions still matter today, the heads of students at this HBCU shoot straight up, with smiles on their faces and praise for "that brother/sister." Yes, as in the media, a greater Black presence in curricula in the form of agents of history, not just victims, can make a difference for self-respect and for the image both Black and White people have of Black people in the broader culture.

In this context, it is necessary to speak to a critique of-ten heard in academic environments and in the media about "Black studies" at the undergraduate and graduate school levels. The existence of these departments has set off fierce debate, with two main camps arguing against these departments. Some scholars—ensconced in the relativism that per-meates much study in the humanities since Immanuel Kant in the nineteenth century—teach that we can never perceive an objective truth about reality.[22] These relativists thus claim that you need a special department to study Black history, totally divorced from global and national history in terms of the curriculum covered and the personnel necessary to understand it correctly from a Black perspective. This sort of relativism is certainly a barrier to real dialogue and mutual understanding, which we need for people to cooperate. We won't rid this world of racism with that kind of thinking. With that kind of separatism, in fact, we are more likely to let racism continue, all the while saying we deplore it.

In the other camp, you have more blatant (although perhaps unwitting) racists who contend that Black studies is bad for American unity. They say that it's time we did away with all of these "Hyphen-Americans." This is quite peculiar if you look at how various ethnic communities are treated in places such as New York City. Consider that Americans whose families have come from Ireland, Italy, Norway, or Germany—in short, anywhere in Europe—are given no trouble today for learning about and celebrating the

---

22.   Immanuel Kant, *Critique of Pure Reason* (1781), I.1; II.III.

ethnicity and the heritage of the "old country." Why, then, do we begrudge this celebration to Black people, and even to recent waves of Spanish-speaking immigrants? The very fact that we never hear laments about Dutch courses at Calvin College in Grand Rapids, Michigan, or Norwegian literature at St. Olaf College in Minnesota, while laments about Afro-centric studies echo in the ivory towers and in the right-wing media, says it all.

One other related matter emerges at this point: Why is the very presence of Black organizations, like fraternities and sororities, businesses, special interest groups, and even churches, a reality that is to be challenged? Is this complaint an indication of the failure to overcome racism? Some might answer that their presence is ultimately a barrier to racial healing and humanizing reconciliation. But note that having such "local organizations" is not contrary to the model for successfully evolving groups suggested by Ostrom, if such groups are part of a larger society. Let's go back to our previous characterization of the American city prior to World War II. It was always okay to be immersed in your ethnic neighborhood; you were still part of the city. But you needed that time and the security of the ethnic neighborhood to feel confident and make you feel you were not alone. The Dutch, the Italians, the Swedes, the Norwegians, and more always had and still have such groups in the United States. Why all the controversy when Black communities have such organizations? We know why.

Let's return to how we run our schools and implement flawed curricula. We have already observed the middle-class, largely White bias of the educational system. By providing a curriculum which includes a significant amount of content unfamiliar to the disadvantaged student, whether inner-city or rural, the school itself creates a climate that is counterproductive to the student's success. Then there is the problem of the bias in our schools toward children with well-developed frontal cortexes, who have the emotional control to be able to sit still and a better ability to forge new brain connections and assimilate new information than a kid growing up with the anxieties of poverty and unsafe neighborhoods.

How can we make our schools more inviting places for children from poor neighborhoods? Remember that Black kids are more likely, in comparison to their White counterparts, to be negatively impacted by these dynamics, rendering our schools not just classist but also racially biased. Curriculum changes and cultural sensitivity, as already suggested, are a good starting point. We could even make immigrant and poor children more at home with the stories of Samuel Ramirez, founder of the first Hispanic banking firm in the U.S., Nydia Velázquez, first Hispanic Congresswoman, and Starbucks chairman and CEO Howard Schultz, a White man who grew up in public housing. These kinds of changes can benefit all students.

Best practices for how to deliver this curriculum are showing up in schools throughout the nation, such as in Coleman A. Young Elementary School in Detroit and the school districts of Reno, Nevada; Springfield, Massachusetts; and Sacramento, California. These districts have succeeded in making schools a less foreign space by meeting students and their parents right where they are and in their own communities. Home visits by administrators and teachers can build the kind of bridge to the poor that we do not normally experience if the administration's investment is confined to the eight hours of daily instruction within the four walls of the classroom. These visits open doors for dialogue and constructive engagement on all sides—the student, the parent, and the faculty member. Evidence shows that when schools conduct home visits to families, both attendance and classroom behavior of children improve.

But what to do about the slower development of the executive function of the brain in students who have endured anxieties caused by impoverished conditions and unsafe circumstances? First, educators must stop blaming students for these realities and disciplining them for what's presumed as bad behavior. We propose finding alternative instruction that allows for further investigation and communication with the students. Strategies include more writing exercises, as the frontal lobe is especially activated and the negative responses of the amygdala are disrupted when we are writing.[23] Peer tutoring and allowing movement by disadvantaged children during a lesson are also proven best practices.[24] These practices do not negate the impact of racism but can affirm some elements of Black culture.

It is hard to overstate the importance of the oral tradition in Black culture.[25] The expectation that disadvantaged students do more writing does not negate or attempt to override this method of communicating and learning. The two can be done in tandem, encouraging students to tell the

---

23. Matthew D. Lieberman et al., "Putting Feelings into Words: Affect Labeling Disrupts Amygdala Activity in Response to Affective Stimuli," *Psychological Science* 18(5) (2007): pp. 421–428.

24. Paul Gorski, *Reaching and Teaching Students in Poverty: Strategies for Erasing the Opportunity Gap*, second edition (New York and London: Teachers College Press, 2018).

25. Michael L. Hecht, Ronald L. Jackson, and Sidney A. Ribeau, *African American Communication: Exploring Identity and Culture* (Milton Park: Routledge, 2002).

stories of their heritage while also writing them down. This allows for free expression and also teaches them how to edit and revise language, both spoken and written. Peer tutoring is also compatible with Black cultural values, including the belief that personhood takes place in community—consider the proverb that "it takes a village to raise a child" (believed to be of African origin). Arranging for students to tutor their peers provides occasions for disadvantaged students to feel like "somebody" and apply what they're learning, while peers getting tutored need not feel so lost when it is one of their own doing the instructing.

We also ought not to discount how the student who does not yet have the neurological tools to sit still for nearly an hour is more likely to listen to instruction if there are structured opportunities for movement. Our schools can and should make all these things happen. Even if we implement these practices, though, it will not lead to an overnight transformation in our schools or in students. There is hope, however. Even with a late start in brain development, given plenty of repetition, the brain can change and new neural pathways and connections can be forged over time.

This is precisely what creating a new ethos in our schools, pertaining to our engagement with students who are considered "unruly"—a disproportionate number of whom are Black—could accomplish. Once we no longer blame them and instead recognize that a lot of their "issues" are not of their own making, we can create learning environments in which they have a chance to thrive, and our schools might start to become a little less classist and a little less racist.

Whether these suggestions are something about which all readers can agree, we can at least agree that educators, parents, and students are supposed to be on the same team.

But let's be suspicious about why these insights about the effects of poverty on students are not already widely acknowledged in the educational establishment, in the wider culture, and in the media. We can begin by bringing this information, and how and why to use it, to the relevant stakeholders in a way they cannot willfully ignore.

Fighting Racism in Health Care

Another urgent challenge that hampers our ability to build a collective collaboration is inequities in public health. Disparities in health care access for African Americans begin with insurance; they are less likely to have health insurance than whites. There is also a severe lack of access to health resources as well. In Georgia, for instance, more than half of the 159 counties do not have enough primary care physicians to serve all their residents. Many of the states with the largest Black populations in the nation, like Mississippi, Oklahoma, Texas, and Arkansas, also rank toward the bottom of health care performance in the nation. This is not a coincidence; intentional public policy decisions have been made that continue to deliver negative health impacts for communities most impacted by lack of access.

The medical community needs to have the most recent data about access to health care constantly in their view; to a large extent that is already standard practice, so the public needs this information too. This brings us to one of the biggest political fights of this generation—access to affordable health care. We need to ensure that all people can afford health insurance and health care, pushing back against federal efforts to capitalize on disparate health outcomes and fighting against campaigns to gut the Affordable Care Act.

It could benefit us to adopt the single-payer system like most other industrialized nations.

If everyone had guaranteed income and was paid a living wage, then health care access would immediately improve. It is important to note, though, that although affordable health insurance is critical to addressing racial inequities, equitable access and patient care is even more urgent. Regarding the disparities between the treatment of Black and White patients, we need to get our frontal cortexes, particularly those of medical staff, working in order to stop seeing Black patients as "other" and to take their symptoms and needs seriously. As with the other disturbing problems addressed in this chapter, health care providers and administrators must be aware of and empowered to meaningfully address the tendency of medical staff to wrongfully dismiss Black patients' concerns. Together we need to alleviate the racism-induced stresses that are experienced in the health care system, especially by Black women during maternal care, in order to improve health outcomes and reduce premature ageing at a cellular level.

Widespread recognition of the medical data on how poverty impacts health is also crucial. The National Urban League has instituted a study in Maryland and Pennsylvania examining health care treatment in relation to the patient's present economic situation. Do we need to prod medical practitioners to keep these connections in mind? In the final analysis, eliminating poverty and economic stress and eliminating the tensions African Americans feel in encounters with police, in the educational establishment, and on the job will make them and the nation healthier. Does not evolution, or the survival of the fittest and of our species, demand that we find ways to do this? In a way, now, we are talking politics.

Increasing Black Power in Politics

One of the greatest challenges to correcting the disparate realities of racism is found in political power, or the lack of it. Stokely Carmichael said that Black Power—group power, not as individuals—is what would ultimately free Black people from the chains of racial oppression. If Black organizers continue working to mobilize their communities to build their own institutions and create their own identities, then racism loses its power. This possibility, of course, gets White hackles up.

The accusation of separatism in response to the call for building "Black power" was conveniently used by conservatives to weaken White support for Civil Rights causes since the 1960s. On those terms, Martin Luther King, Jr., expressed concerns about "Black Power" connoting separatism or violence.[26] He also embraced the idea of Blacks claiming their power economically and politically with the vote, not through separation but through coalitions. Black Power is about African Americans exercising the power to define themselves, not letting the media or other groups define who they are.[27]

Organizations like the Congressional Black Caucus, the Black Economic Alliance, Black Lives Matter, other civil rights organizations, and even Black faith institutions inside predominantly White denominations embody this sort of Black Power. As a former state leader of NAACP, Woodall adds that though having institutions and spaces of liberative organizing are necessary, having these organizations alone does not free Black people from the chains of racism. Even in these organizations that work toward liberative ends, they, too, often fall

26. King, "Where Do We Go From Here?" pp. 566, 572–573.
27. King, "Where Do We Go From Here?" pp. 578–580, 582, 585–586.

victim to the very human qualities, such as ego-driven leadership, corporate greed, and interpersonal biases, that hinder us from achieving the kinds of success that impact the much broader Black-White collaborative effort.

Nevertheless, we must work on organizing and recruiting Black communities through the civic engagement and electoral process, as this will be especially important to counter the latest legislative efforts to suppress the votes of Black and Brown voters, known by voting and civil rights advocates as Jim Crow 2.0. There are at least some ways around Republican demands for proper identification of voters, for example.

For the impoverished and working poor who are unable to drive, most states provide identification cards through the Department of Motor Vehicles for those with proof of residence, Social Security number, and proof of citizenship. In some states, independent resource providers can secure identification for the homeless for a fee. Obviously, this will not get everyone voting, but at least we can put a dent in the exclusion. The racism in these laws isn't in the ID requirements themselves. Those who find it difficult to meet these requirements tend to be poor voters, some in rural communities where DMV locations and hours are prohibitive. The racism in photo ID requirements is evident in that a disproportionate amount of the voters who face challenges in meeting those requirements are Black. They are disparately impacted by the extra steps that they must undertake in order successfully to meet the requirements to vote—a civil liberty that is supposed to be available to us all.

Yes, separate Black initiatives make a lot of sense. But as King wanted, and like the insights of Elinor Ostrom seem to promote, it is in the interests of all these organizations and their activities to remain in dialogue with broader communities (what Ostrom called polycentric governance).

One desirable political agenda which can only come to fruition through collaboration is cutting costs of election campaigns, for as noted the present system allows undue influence on legislative decisions by the rich. The public financing of elections, like in Connecticut, can take away the influence of corporate lobbyists so that the poor and working classes (Black and white) matter more. For human beings doing the right thing, it really is all about cooperation. This is how to stop racism and why racism must stop; it's about human survival. If we all don't win, we lose.

Beating Racism in the Media and in Pop Culture

Representation within mass media has been one of the most notable forms of cultural affirmation of American racism. Seeing creatives (an inclusive term used to describe the diverse range of skills and professions in the entertainment and arts) of color gain inclusion in content for television, broadcast journalism, and even Hollywood (like *Just Mercy*) and Broadway (think of *Hamilton*) provides necessary visibility in a consumer-dominated society. The more we see Black people in front of and behind the camera as writers, directors, narrators, and performers of these stories, the likelier we are to encounter a more favorable portrayal of Blacks in society overall.

Even the ways Black people are disproportionately represented in news coverage has been identified as problematic. Media content that highlights Black people as other than violent and/or criminal—instead portraying them as doctors, educators, and even heroes—will counteract the current imbalance of stories of Black criminals. Along with more positive images of Black people in movies and TV shows, this emphasis will help people become more acclimated to seeing non-White leads within our society at large, thus reaffirming the humanity of the non-White other. It will still take generations of intentional inclusion of Black creatives to erase racist prejudice on the big screen.

The media's range of inclusion of Black creativity and skill is a perfect example of how when we cooperate, everybody wins, especially when a multicultural audience can be generated. The economic implications of increasing visibility and making space for characteristically excluded Black creatives are great especially if we can improve the economic standing of African Americans to make them not just consumers, but producers and owners of these products as well.

Given the level of discrimination against Black entrepreneurs noted (recall the challenges Black business owners face in getting loans and the resulting loss of years of wealth accumulation), we can make the case that the media should be amplifying Black-owned businesses, which cater to the Black market, by raising the desirability of their products. This attention could be an effective way of ensuring that their hyped presence builds toward reparations via increased profits. Reparations would acknowledge generations of racist exclusion and contribute to the sustainable success of the Black media and entrepreneurial community.

In addition, expanded opportunities for Black-owned businesses and Black workers can also benefit non-Black businesses. Heather McGhee, in her book *The Sum of Us*, emphasizes that everybody wins when media and market shares are enlarged. Businesses may see a more diverse labor and talent force as we feed the aspirations and imaginations of young Black kids who begin to see more of themselves in positions of power and in roles of respect in the media.

How do we get to this new era of the screen? We have already seen how social pressure helps, with campaigns like #OscarsSoWhite encouraging Hollywood to become more sensitive to issues of diverse representation and racial inclusion. Economic pressure is another way to get the media to provide more positive Black role models.

The organization Color of Change is already working on providing more positive Black role models fighting injustice in communities and nationwide. You may want to consider affiliating with them if this is a priority for you and your goals. When you are considering working with an organization like this, examine whether the organization reflects economist Elinor Ostrom's principles for an evolving business. If you cannot find an established group whose identity and purpose are right for you, why not start a movement of your own? No matter which you choose, we should agree that something must be done to impact the negative branding of Black people in this country. If we sit still on this one, we've caved in to racism.

Black-White Collaboration: An Evolutionary Process

This chapter has put a lot of possible anti-racist proposals on the table. Doing just one or two of them in and of themselves will not end racism. As Lonnie King, a dear friend and leader of the successful Atlanta Student Movement in the 1960s, often said: "The struggle against racism is not a sprint. It's a long-distance run." Famed American theologian Reinhold Niebuhr offered similar observations. He wrote:

This insinuation of the interests of the self into even the most ideal enterprises and most universal objectives, envisaged in moments of highest rationality, makes hypocrisy an inevitable byproduct of all virtuous endeavor.[28]

This means that, whenever you think justice has been achieved, when it seems to you that racism has ended, be careful. If something in society feels good and just to you, be careful. Chances are it's only good and just for you and your tribe. This is the warning Critical Race Theory so properly issues to us.

Obviously, this is a warning for those who believe the Civil Rights Movement in America has fully accomplished its aims. In the view of many White people, since America has even elected a Black president, we must be a post-racial society. If you are relatively content with the state of things, it may be just because it's good for you, your family, and maybe even Black folks in your network—not for humanity.

Always being aware of our selfishness—part of what Christians call sin—allows us to remain realistic about our struggle against racism. Racial prejudice is, after all, part of our brain's make-up dating back to our early evolution from animals. That's why racism is your and my problem, not just the fault of *those* bad people. But if we truly continue the evolutionary cycle which has characterized our species, cooperating in ever more fulfilling ways, then we'll see racism as a problem for all of us. And if we ever evolve that far as humans (maybe guided by our spirituality), then we'll really begin to put racism on the run. We really are all in this together! But we are not there yet. You and I have not done (and never will do, on this side of life) enough about racism.

Yes, the warnings of Critical Race Theory merely echo ʌur Constitution and the Christian view of sin. But we note ʰᵃt we disagree with the theory's proponents if their

—

p. 45.

warning entails that we ought not to play the game of cooperation across racial lines. Our constitutional system and the continuing process of evolution keep summoning us to cooperation. Hope (the King Dream, seen in moments of spirituality and contemplation when we sense our oneness with all that is) will never die, not as long as we remain human. And that hope and vision, for people of faith, is rooted in God, but when you are in touch with the cooperative aspects of your humanity it will inspire you even more. It inspires us "to keep on keepin' on."

New City Press

New City Press is one of more than 20 publishing houses sponsored by the Focolare, a movement founded by Chiara Lubich to help bring about the realization of Jesus' prayer: "That all may be one" (John 17:21). In view of that goal, New City Press publishes books and resources that enrich the lives of people and help all to strive toward the unity of the entire human family. We are a member of the Association of Catholic Publishers.

www.newcitypress.com
202 Comforter Blvd.
Hyde Park, New York

Periodicals
Living City Magazine
www.livingcitymagazine.com

Scan to join our mailing list
for discounts and promotions
or go to www.newcitypress.com
and click on "join our email list."

47